"Courtney writes with such flour[...] it virtually impossible for you to p[...] rue the time at which you need t[...] characterizations and even more [...] ensure that this is worthy of any bookshelf."

Angela Freebeef – Modern Classics Book Circle
(Uk & Europe)

"A rip-roaring rollercoaster ride of emotions. Hilariously funny, extremely sad, and at times deeply disturbing. Courtney's anecdotal narrative compels and repulses and at the same time had me in fits of belly laughter. The transition from the naivety of a youth spent growing up in the '80s, and the comparisons with a drug-fuelled '90s and the harsh reality of being a *Grown Up* are unmissable reading. Prepare to applaud, laugh and cry as a new writing super talent emerges from nowhere. Fabulous, a sure fire hit, but don't lend it to your Gran."

Nellie Shoesmith – Baboo Monthly

"This is *Black* comedy at its deepest, darkest, blackest ever."

Sandy Handwarmer – Mad Dog Publications

"Forget the '60s… if you remember the '90s, you definitely weren't there."

Alberto Kellog – Time and Motion Magazine

"One can only wonder if Courtney has drawn from personal experiences or if he is just the master of the tall story… nevertheless, this is contemporary literature at its horrifying best."

Hupert Interface – Up The Junction Periodical

"Did anybody ask for this crap to be written? No, they didn't… Courtney needs to… *FUCK OFF*."

Ronnie O'McVanguard – The All Celtic Book Organisation

"Think *Catcher in the Rye*… think *Alice in Wonderland*… think *The Godfather*… This is *FUCK* all like any of those literary classics… It makes me sick to the pit of my stomach."

Anonymous Entry
(Possibly by Leonard Stool Off The Telly)

"Brilliant… just bloody brilliant… I can't believe it… He was always good at writing though, at school and that."

Jackie – Daz's Mam

"I was crying with laughter. A top read."

Jules – Daz's Sister

"I can't make head nor tail of it… I think it might all be lies y'know… It's OK… I've read better… Is it supposed to be true? … I never know when to believe the little feck… It passes the time I suppose."

John – Daz's Dad

"Heavy going at times but the pace at which Courtney writes keeps you enthralled. It hurtles along at breakneck speed… I was sweating reading it. The dialogue is excellently interspersed with humour and terror, often in the *same* paragraph. His ability to horrify and disgust, yet at the same time make you keel over with laughter, is an accolade to his talent as a writer."

Franklin D Hooverbelt
– YouKnowWho Books and Magazines

Voted Just for Fun Magazine's Book of the Century

NINE FOOT TALL

DAZ COURTNEY

The Book Guild Ltd

First published in Great Britain in 2019 by
The Book Guild Ltd
9 Priory Business Park
Wistow Road, Kibworth
Leicestershire, LE8 0RX
Freephone: 0800 999 2982
www.bookguild.co.uk
Email: info@bookguild.co.uk
Twitter: @bookguild

Typeset in Minion Pro

Printed and bound in the UK by TJ International, Padstow, Cornwall

ISBN 978 1912881 925

British Library Cataloguing in Publication Data.
A catalogue record for this book is available from the British Library.

Dedicated to Jacqueline Rose, a rose by name and by nature.

For Kerri
All the best
Enjoy.

Daz..

X

CONTENTS

PROLOGUE

The late 1980s, 1988 in particular, saw the emergence of a new type of music; it came from Chicago and they called it house. With its thumping beats and repetitive rhythms, it captured the imaginations of a generation. But with this new music there also came new drugs, and at the forefront was ecstasy. Along with amphetamines and cocaine, these drugs not only became commonplace, they became respectable. It is estimated that by 1995 over 2.5 million people used so-called "recreational" drugs every single weekend in England. Over half that amount came from the Yorkshire area.

> THE WICKED SHALL FALL BY THEIR
> OWN WICKEDNESS
> The Bible – The Book of Proverbs,
> Chapter 11, Verse 5

MARCH 5TH 1999 — AGED 32

Whenever you read a book where some arsehole is getting out of jail, they always act as though they're the Count of Monte Cristo or summat, man, all artistic and shit. Something like this:

> There's something strange about being released from prison, the "shovel", dreamlike even.
> From the blackness of the jail, the doors open, and then…
> It's the brightest day you've ever witnessed.
> Blinding sunshine.
> The dew on the grass is glistening.
> Sparkling like diamonds.
> It's like being born.

Ha ha, very poetic, don't you think? Now, all that's probably true if you've just done some twenty-year *Shawshank Redemption* kinda shit, but I hadn't – I'd only been in just shy of seven months. But know this – I was in no rush to go back to the fucker.

'You'll be back, lad.'

This guard was only about twenty years old, if that, and he's calling *me* lad. I've got a good twelve years on him. As he slammed the door behind me, I didn't look back, nor did I even dignify him with an answer. I just smiled to myself, walked calmly to the station and thought, *The fuck I will.*

A two-hour train journey to get home would give me just long enough to reflect, to wonder what, just what, it was that brought me to this. I looked through the windows at the winter countryside as it hurtled past, and closed my eyes.

SUMMER 1996 — AGED 29

'Gaz. There's a call for you.'

Eric the barman looked disgruntled as he passed me the phone – how dare anyone ring during Happy Hour when he's rushed off his feet? He's a grumpy fucker.

'Yeah? Who dat?' I asked.

People can laugh when something isn't even the remote bit funny, at the most inappropriate times. Could be a lack of diplomacy. Could be nerves. Or shock. Yes, this must have been shock.

'Hiya Gaz, it's Rick.' It was my younger brother Ricky.

'Hiya, Little Bruv. What's up?'

'It's me nana, Gaz man. Ha ha. She's dead. Ha ha ha. She just died.'

'Why the fuck are you laughing? Me nana's died. And you're *laughing*?'

'I can't help it, Gaz. Just come up. All the family are here and we're waiting for the undertaker to come.'

'Right, love. I'll be straight there. Bye.'

I leaned across the bar, forced a smile and...

'Eric... a double brandy and Coke please.'

I'd only ever seen dead people in the movies, y'know, shot to death and shit like that. This was different. My nana Maggie. Oh God. My poor nana Maggie. Sleeping.

Not unlike her morphine-induced sleep across the last few months. But this would be for always. Her lips were slightly open, pursed.

I kissed them.

And the funeral director took her away.

Forever.

'Anita, 'I whispered in my auntie Anita's ear as the undertaker slowly drove away down the street, 'I need to speak to you in private.'

She took me into my nana Maggie's bedroom, all floral and perfumed.

My auntie Anita. She had cared for my nana since the cancer took a grip; it showed in her face. Still kindly, but ageing fast.

She smiled at me inquisitively.

'Yes, Gaz? Are you okay?'

Was I about to offer a hug, some reassuring words of thanks for the way she had sacrificed her own life to care for my nana Maggie?

'How much of me nana's morphine have you got left? I can get a good price for it. We'll go halves.'

If you've ever had a look from someone… a look that says *You must be desperate. And sad. But I still love you…* then this was that look.

'It's all in that drawer over there. Take it. Do what you bleedin' want with it. Keep the bloody money.'

She wept.

I emptied the drawer.

And left.

CHAPTER ONE

—

DIY

A CAT WILL EAT FISH BUT WON'T WET ITS FEET
13th-century French proverb

WINTER 1995 — AGED 28

'He's a good lad, really.'

My mother explained this to her pal in a not so sure way; she knew I was up to no good, but she didn't see any harm in what I was doing. I was a kind-hearted villain to her. Robin Hood.

'He's a *drug dealer*, Jackie; all the young'uns on the estate get Es off him. Everybody knows except you it seems.'

My mam would always shrug these kind of absurd comments off, make excuses for me, anything but realise that everyone was right. I was a bastard. That was it. End of.

Anyway, I *wasn't* a drug dealer. Not really. Drug dealers have got loads of money, they drive flash cars, they sell heroin to school kids. Don't they?

A bit of Billy and a few Es doesn't make a drug dealer. Does it?

Now, being a drug dealer and selling drugs are two completely different situations. I fell into the latter.

Here's how it goes…

You're the self-proclaimed "World's number one DJ and Porno Legend"! You work every night of the week entertaining the masses until the early hours. You want to unwind after work… but it's 2am… What do you do? You go to a club until 9am, that's what! Then what do you do? Yep, you got it in one… You go to a party until four in the afternoon. Go home… eat a snack… go back to work at 7.30pm, and so it goes on. Fantastic!

A lifestyle to envy? *Of course it is!*

There's only one "minor problem". Three or four weeks of this and you will die of exhaustion. I know – I'll take something to make me lively all the time. I mean, I owe it to my paying customers, don't I?

A tired DJ is a shit DJ. A miserable DJ makes his crowd miserable. A miserable crowd won't come back. I'm never tired and never miserable. Why? Because I know "a man who knows a dog". That's why.

Being behind the decks is like a drug – you get addicted, it's true, and you feel famous, even though you're only in the tiny bars of Leeds, yeah, you feel *famous*.

Everybody knows who you are, everybody wants to buy you a drink, everybody wants you to go to bed with them and everybody wants to give you drugs.

Sounds good to me.

Buying drugs to me was part of the job; I had to stay awake, right? Be happy.

Everybody had drugs if you wanted some. My drug was Billy.

Billy. Whizz. Speed. Fast. Quick. Phet. Powder. Pink champagne. Paste.

Amphetamines, whatever name you gave it, it still kept you awake; no matter what you call it, it still makes you the most talkative person in the entire universe; no matter what you call it, it still makes you the happiest person this side of a Butlin's redcoat.

No matter what you call it, it would make you paranoid. I started off getting a couple of "wraps" a week, but as the lifestyle got more hectic so did the need for more "gear".

This is where "the man" came in. We all knew him, we all knew that you could get more than the odd wrap from him. You could get as much as you liked. That would do me just fine and dandy.

It was cheaper to buy in bulk. So I did.

Just for me, mind. I'm not a drug dealer, after all.

It doesn't take a genius to notice when someone is "off their head".

Everyone knew. The bar bosses knew, the punters knew, they all knew.

But although they knew, they didn't care.

I was lively. I was funny. Hilarious. I played the best tunes. I packed them in.

So what if he's off his nut? He does the job and he does it well.

'Can I have some of what you're on, Gaz?'

You'd always get the odd punter asking for stuff, but I only bought enough for myself, enough to last the week.

But if you get asked often enough, you begin to think – no, you begin to *know* – that you could make a bit of money selling some on to the punters.

A few wraps to him, a couple to her, some for the girls who call in for half an hour on a Friday before they go clubbing. No big deal.

But news gets around.

Pretty soon you're "the man". The one who can get the gear.

Right, so I buy an ounce a week. This equates to twenty-eight grammes; ten quid a gramme means two hundred and eighty quid for me, less the hundred that I gave for it, so I'm one eighty clear. Right?

Wrong!

It's right, I do buy an ounce a week and it does cost me hundred quid, but here's the gig – I get it "laid on", on credit if you will. So far so good, no layout, sell the stuff, pay the man his hundred quid back.

Perfect.

I then proceed to eat half of it myself, sell some, spend the proceeds like I think I'm Peter Stringfellow and, yep, you've guessed it. I still owe the man a hundred notes.

I know. I'll get another ounce "laid on" and pay him from the proceeds of that. Problem solved.

Eat. Sell. Stringfellow. Owe twice as fucking much.

And the beat goes on.

'A grand you owe me, Gaz. You keep fobbing me off. I like you, Gaz, you're funny. But if you don't pay me what you owe, well, let's just say…I won't like you anymore. I won't think you're funny. Friday, I want my money.' The Man could be a scary cunt to say the least.

Fuck! It's Monday. Who in their right fucking mind wants to buy drugs during the week, besides me? I need to pay this debt. Fuck.

I tend to have this habit, which must be annoying to other people, of falling into very big barrels of shite and coming out smelling of the proverbial roses.

So, out of the blue, I get a call from an old acquaintance, Barry. I haven't seen him for over a year.

'Hi Gaz, it's Barry, long time no see. Look, I won't beat about the bush, I need some gear for me and me mates. We're off to work away and we need about five ounces of whizz and about a hundred tabs of acid. Can you do it?'

'Yeah course, man, when do you need them?' I replied, too cool for school.

'By Wednesday. We go Friday.'

'No problem. It'll be one fifty an ounce for the Billy and a quid a tab; that's eight fifty altogether. You got the money?'

'Yeah, we've all clubbed together.'

'Wednesday, then. Sorted, Barry me old pal.'

Fuck. Fuck. Fuck. Fuck. Fuck. Fuck. Fuck.

He's got eight hundred and fifty quid waiting for me, and I've only got about thirty quid's worth of Billy to my name and I haven't even seen a tab of acid in three years. I can't get anything off The Man – that'd be taking the complete piss.

Fuck. Think, Gaz, think.

Eureka!

Now, here's the deal.

I go to the chemist. I buy five boxes of glucose, two cartons of paracetamol. Then next door to the post office – a child's £1.99 printing set, some coloured card and fifty medium-sized resealable Jiffy bags, you know? The kind that shirt buttons come in.

Shopping bill:

»   Glucose x 5 @ 99p each = £4.95
»   Paracetamol x 2 @ 75p each = £1.50
»   Printing set = £1.99
»   Card@ 5p per sheet x 2 = 10p
»   Jiffy bags x 50 = £2.10

Total.£10.64

The best £10.64 I would ever spend. Without a shadow of a Doubting Thomas. This is it, Gaz, no worries. The Man's gonna get most of his money. Zippity day!

Right, into the kitchen, get out a big bowl, in goes the glucose, crush the paracetamol to add bitterness, mix it all together, oh, and don't forget, throw in the thirty quid of Billy that I've got left over. Mix, stir, mix, crush, weigh it into five ounces and put it into Jiffy bags.

Job done.

We now have five ounces of Billy. Of course I'll tell them that it's been cut, rude not to. I just won't say how *much* it's been cut. Ha har!

Now it's time to be a little more artistic.

I get a Stanley knife and score the card so that it has a hundred tiny squares on it, take out the printing set, a little rubber stamper really, not much cop but does the trick. I opt for the little swallow picture coz it's very pretty. Ha! Stamp stamp stamp…

Place folded card into Jiffy bags and, Hey Presto! A hundred "Blue Swallows", the latest tabs of acid to come from Amsterdam. Ha!

Do-it-yourself drugs!

Let's go meet Barry.

Like I say, I haven't seen Barry for over a year; he moved to a little town a couple of hours' drive away.

I arrange to meet him at two in the afternoon, outside the train station, lots of people about. If he susses me he won't make a fuss in public, will he?

I'll go in the car with two of my friends, walk over to Barry, who'll be alone, and do a really sly swap of goods and money by appearing to shake hands and give him a hug. Exchange done, quick retreat back to the car. Drive home. Sorted.

So, it's Wednesday. We pull up to the station and there's Barry leaning on a railing.

I get out, heart beating like Johnny Bongos, walk over and *Fuck!*

He's got two guys with him, proper fucking meatheads too. *Fuck. Think.*

I look really nervous and shifty as I approach him, looking over my shoulder and the like.

'Barry, we've gotta be quick.'

I point to a random car pulling into the station. It's got three big guys in it and drives to the upper end of the concourse.

'That car has followed us all the way here. I'm sure I've seen 'em before. Pigs, man. Quick, let's do it and get fucked off.'

Barry and his steroid-busting mates get really nervous now. It's gonna come on top.

I give him a hug, swap goods and look around…

'Go on, quick, Barry man. Fuck off into the crowd.'

They disappear. I run back to the car.

Screech off.

Back to Leeds.

Laughing.

Eight and a half hundred quid in my pocket.

Smelling of fucking roses. Ha!

—

CHAPTER TWO

IT'S A FAR CRY FROM MONDAY NIGHT AT TIFFANY'S

Stayin' Alive – Bee Gees, 1977

Up until the age of around fourteen, I was what could only be described as a geek. A nerd.

A swot. A spod. A spoff.

An all boys' school, an all boys' *Catholic* school, believe it or not, brought me right out of my shell. I didn't just come out of it, I smashed my way out like a baby fucking eagle.

You see, the fact that there are no girls there can make you go one of two ways. You can either turn gay. No ta. Or you can spend your every waking hour, and most of your sleeping ones, thinking and dreaming and wishing and hoping for the chance to meet some of the fairer sex.

Absence truly does make the heart grow fonder. I knew that girls were my vocation in life; the only problem was, the only ones I knew were my mam and my sister.

Something had to change.

SUMMER 1981 – AGED 14

Monday night at Tiff's, that's Tiffany's, the largest nightclub in Leeds. It even had a great big plastic palm tree at the side of the dance floor. It was *the* night, the place to be. It didn't matter to us that it was for under-eighteens only. That they didn't serve beer. We could get our own before we went in. It just didn't matter.

You see, Tiff's was something special – your mates were there, the music, the lights and the girls.

Yes, the girls.

Hundreds of them.

I'd hardly spoken to a girl, let alone kissed one, but Tiff's was my starter for ten.

All boys' school by day. Every fucking day. Tiff's by night.

It's my first night there and I've gone with Glenroy and Martin, a couple of mates who knew the score. Glenroy was black with no neck, dressed like Leroy from *Fame*, and Martin was white and skinny, just like me. Except Martin had a kilt on. Well, it is the '80s.

They had been hundreds of times, or so they told me, and they got laid every week, so they told me. But I don't believe that anyone who wears a kilt is *ever* gonna get laid.

I walk in and there's strobes turning you into robots, and reds and blues and greens, and my head's spinning already. Soft Cell, Depeche Mode, Human League. Spinning. Nothing to do with the two bottles of cider before we walked in – no, it was the atmosphere.

There were girls *everywhere* and, get this, they were coming up to me, coming up to *me*, The Spod. In their miniskirts and teabag tee-shirts. This, I thought, is for me.

Dancing, swaying, kissing and fumbling. Just what the Good Lord intended every red-blooded fourteen-year-old to do.

Then it's over.

The trouble with Tiff's is that it closes at 10pm, with it being under-eighteens and all, so it has to… to make way for the grown-ups. We *were* grown up, so it wasn't fair; it finished just when you started to have fun. I'd go home and my head would still be spinning, buzzing, telling my mam about the night, leaving some things out of course – there are certain things that you just don't tell your mam.

It became a ritual for us on a Monday. We thought we were the main men. We weren't, but we thought we were. I was no longer a geek. I was Gaz the *Man*.

BANK HOLIDAY MONDAY – 31ST AUGUST 1981

I'm loving life – it's the summer holidays, it's hot, no school, *and* it's Monday! Tiff's night. So here's my plan for tonight: call for Glenroy and then go meet Claire. I'd met Claire at Tiff's last week and she looked just like Bardot, man. I'd arranged to meet her outside Tiff's. Yes, I'm loving life.

First stop, Glenroy's house. I gave a hard knock on his door and almost instantly the door flung open. It was Glenroy's mam, a big handsome woman you might say, portly, with a headscarf around her Swede, in a kind of *Gone with the Wind* style, a real homely looking West Indian lady. She was eating a lime like an apple! Biting through the skin and everything, man.

'Hail, bwoy, wah yuh wa?'

Now, I'd spoken to Mrs Glenroy, as I called her, lots of times, and I still had no clue what she was on about, man.

'Hello Mrs Glenroy. Is Glenroy coming out please?'

Mrs Glenroy glared at me wide-eyed, threw her lime in a bin by the door and then, with one hand on her hip and the other on the door frame, turned her head into the house and shouted, nay screamed, upstairs:

'GlenRye, yuh bredrin at di doa. Him wa kno eff yuh come out.' Then she turned her head back to me, still glaring. 'Him nah be lang, san. An how many time me tell yuh? Mi name *not* Mrs GlenRye.'

At this she made a strange noise as though she were kissing her teeth and waddled back into the house mumbling and cursing under her breath.

I had a little giggle to myself and then Glenroy appeared in the doorway wearing a red silk robe!

'Alright, Gaz man, what's happening?' Glenroy had a Yorkshire accent, not a crazy one like his mam.

'You know what, Glenroy man? I have never understood a fucking word your mam has ever said, mate.'

'Ha ha,' Glenroy laughed. 'Don't worry about her, Gaz man, she's from Barbados. And she's depressed beyond tablets. She makes us taste her food before she eats it.'

I laughed at that statement, puzzling as it was.

'Ha ha, Glenroy man. I don't even know what that means but you crack me up, pal. Anyway, man, how come you're not ready? You're not gonna wear *that* to Tiff's, are you, man? C'mon, I've gotta meet that Claire bird soon.'

'Nah, Gaz man, I'm not coming.'

'What? Just coz I'm meeting that lass? Aw come on, man, what's up wi yer?'

'Nah, mate, nowt to do wi' that bird, man, she's sweet. I'm just not coming. It's shit.'

'Shit? You love it, man, you have a right laugh normally. What's happened, bud? Has your mam been slashing her arms again?'

Glenroy tightened the belt on his red silk robe, looked behind him into his house and came out into the garden.

'Ya know what it is, Gaz man? It's nowt to do with me mam's arms. I'm not coming coz it's full of fuckin' *n*****s, man, that's why, too many for my liking.'

I gave a nervous little giggle and thought for a second, and then said:

'Ha ha, man, what you talkin' about? N*****s? You're a—'

He cut me off mid-sentence.

'Gaz, don't you dare call me a n*****, man, just don't. I'm not a n*****, I'm black. But them cunts who pick on everyone at Tiff's, they're n*****s, man.'

'I wasn't gonna call you that, pal, I hate that word. You know me, man. I'm not a racialist, but I'm not sure I'm with you, man. You mean them that bully everyone at the other side of the club?'

Now, I knew the lads that he was talking about, you can spot them a mile off, hanging around the geeks and taking their spending money, jumping up and down like fucking baboons at the Space Invader, trying to make some poor spod crash his spaceship so they can bully his last go from him. They could be heard around the place with the unforgettable words: 'Leeeanne me teeeane peeance.' Which, in our language, would translate to: 'Lend me ten pence.' It was their way of extorting money from you by using the premise that it was only a loan. You'd never get the fucker back. In fact, if you were stupid enough to put your hand in your pocket and pull out more than ten pence, then that was it –*Sock!* Bam! Bish! Fat lip, black eye, no bastard money left. I fucking hated the thieving bullying bastards. Kept out of their way. They scared me.

Glenroy continued:

'Yeah, them cunts, man. They give the rest of us black people a bad reputation, man. We're not all like them, they're just fucking n*****s. They've got a bad fucking attitude. Bad fuckin' mazzle. It was n*****s that were rioting a couple of weeks ago in Chapeltown, not black people like the papers said. N*****s.'

Glenroy was right, there had been riots in Chappy a couple of weeks back, it was all over the papers – burning cars and looting and stabbing and shit.

'I just put that down to poverty and socio-economic situations and stuff like that.'

'Nah, fuck that poverty shit, Gaz man, they were just fuckin' lazy thieving chancers. Look at it this way – I wasn't there, was I? I'm black. My mam wasn't there, was she? She's definitely black. Mr Frankland from school wasn't there, was he? He's the blackest man I ever saw. Fat Cheeno and his fat brother weren't there, was they? Fuck knows what colour they are, man, but they most definitely are not white. Were all the old ladies from St Ophelia's Baptist Church there? No, none of 'em wa, man. I'll tell you who wa there – a load of fuckin n*****s making life hard for me in future, making us all look bad. I'm not gonna apologise for them cunts to no-one, man.'

I was still a little confused by his outburst, but he obviously felt strongly about it so I looked up and said:

'So, you not coming, then?'

He shook his head and walked back in his house, kissing his teeth like his depressed Barbadian mam.

So off I toddled to meet Claire, seeing as Glenroy's not coming coz he's racist and Martin's gone to Blackpool with their kid. With his kilt on.

So, I'm here in Tiff's, I've got my girl, gorgeous, just like Bardot, pink leggings around her ankles, it's all sweet. I'm looking sharp too – jet black quiff, crisp white shirt with a frilly front, pressed to perfection, the black pantaloons with the tight bottoms tucked into my pointy toed Robin Hood boots, the great smell of Brut. Fantastic. And yes, we are both a little drunk; could be the night you lose your cherry, Gaz. Could be.

No such fucking luck.

I'm dancing with my girl, Adam and the Ants screaming their little heads off, and I'm busting for a shite. Can you believe this? A hot date and I need to go for a shite. Can't hold it, gotta go.

'Claire, I'm just nipping to the bog. Two minutes.'

Right, I'm off. Sharpish.

Shitting in a public bog has never been my favourite thing in the world, but if you gotta go, then needs must.

I walk into the bogs and there's heaps of guys hanging around, y'know, smoking weed and drinking beer that they sneaked in. Oh, and there are some black guys.

I'm looking for a cubicle with a door that locks and there isn't a single one, all broken. Hellfire, Mr Turd is pushing against the gusset of me scrundies now. Fuck it.

I dive into a cubicle, close the door, drop me trolleys, sit straight down and start to squeeze one out. Bliss. The fact that the door won't lock and I'm having to lean forward to keep it closed with my hand doesn't matter. When you're dying for a crap and it comes out, there is no better fucking feeling. I'm chuckling to myself because I can hear David Bowie and Queen singing *Under Pressure* from the club.

Splash! Turd number one has landed – wet all me arse as well with the splash. I don't care because here comes turd number two, and he is a *beauty* – squeeze, Gaz, get the fucker out.

And then, out of nowhere:

Bang!

The toilet door slams open and hits me right in the fucking eyebrow, blood gushing, pissing out –always does from your eyebrow, man.

'What the fuck?'I exclaimed in utter shock.

I can't believe my fucking eyes. This is unbe-*fucking*-lievable. I'm taking a dump, the fucker is still halfway out of my arse, and there's *King* and fucking *Kong* in the doorway of my cubicle. Two huge black kids... well, they were huge to me. One of them had a hair lip. Some sort of cleft palate or summat.

'Leeeanne me teeeane peeeeeannce, white bwoouy.'

Oh no, man, it was the guys from the other side of the club, the bullies.

'You have *got* to be kiddin' me. I'm having a fucking shite.'

'Monaaaay now, bwoouy.'

I'm getting nervous now, these cunts mean business and I've still got Charlie Brown hanging from me arse, too thick to nip. *Under Pressure* still playing in the club.

'Look, fellas, let me finish me crap and I'll see what I've got in me pockets. Okay. One minute.'

I wave my finger as if to repeat what I just said.

Humiliation is the worst torture known to man. Forget getting red hot needles in your eyes or razors across the bell of your dick, humiliation is the worst, and guess what, these dudes have got it off to a fine fucking art. Completely ignorant to my plea, they each grab a foot, and *Bong!* They pull me straight off the toilet and onto the tiled floor, the "wet through with everyone in the fucking club's piss" floor. This is the most unfunny thing that has ever happened to me. This is not at all nice.

Not only am I sitting in rivers of piss, but the big, fat, creamy turd that was hanging from my sphincter chopped off on the seat when they pulled me off and smeared right up my back. No, not smeared – the only word to describe it is *smathered*, yeh, smathered up my nice new *white* frilly shirt. And I banged me head on the seat, but that wasn't so bad as it was a crappy plastic one.

I get a swift kick to the chin from King, a jab in the cheek from Kong, they rifle me pockets, take my cash, what little I already had, and they fuck off. Laughing.

I manage to stand up, a bit shaken up from the kick and the punch, but fuck that, man, I'm covered in piss, and there is *brown, fuckin', foul, stinking shite* all the way up my back, even on my hair, my lovely hair.

I look in the mirror and I'm a right mess.

And I stink. Of shit.

That right there just sucked the fun right out of my childhood, man.

I limp back out to the dance floor to Claire, still with lots of shite left on me – couldn't wash it all off in the toilet – she sees me, smells me, calls me a dirty little bastard and gets sick over me, big fucking chunky sick as well. Then she runs off crying. Leaving me stood staring at the DJ, who must think he's a funny fucker because he bangs on *Don't You Want Me* by Human League. Har bloody har.

I never saw Claire again as long as I lived. Pity that, she looked like Bardot.

I've no cash, so I have to walk the four miles home.

Stinking.

In the rain.

And the wind.

Glenroy was right though, man, these guys weren't black, they were fucking *n*****s*!

SUMMERTIME 1995 – AGED 28

I've always maintained that "you should beware the little guy". If you go to a nightclub and the bouncer is only five foot tall and the others are all six foot bruise monsters, then you should watch out for the little fella. He's there for a reason. He can do some damage.

I've never been big. Sometimes wish I was, but never have been. Oh well.

But Steve, my mate Steve, my "business" partner, from a distance you'd believe he was nothing. Five foot eight, a very unassuming looking character, like looking at John Hurt.

Drinks with his pinky stuck out and crosses his legs.

But if you get up real close and you can see into his eyes, shark's eyes, then you know, you know he can hurt you.

Bad.

They call him "Unsolved Steve". This name, apparently, is attributed to him because most of the unsolved murders in Leeds are supposedly from his hands.

A black guy once walked over to him in a pub, real mean-looking bastard, Steve with his legs crossed and all, and said to Steve, 'Are you a puff?'

Steve didn't even flinch at this remark, he knew full well that the guy wanted to cause trouble, and just calmly answered with, 'No, mate. Are you a n*****?'

Before anyone even knew what was going on, the black guy was laid on the deck.

A broken bottle stuck in his neck.

Like I said. He can hurt you.

Oh, and he snorts extreme amounts of coke.

Tonight was no exception. I'd had some too, just a little mind. I mean, I'm no drug addict, but Steve had half of Colombia up his nostrils.

We've got to go and pick up some cash; a guy we do business with, Rasta Bill, owes us two hundred quid and he's asked us to meet him in the "blues".

The blues, a shebeen, an after-hours drinking den. Illegal, of course.

These places can be pretty daunting – middle of Chapeltown, the run-down black ghetto of Leeds. Always, and I mean always, run by, and mostly frequented by, blacks.

But that doesn't matter to us.

They're our mates.

Most of 'em.

We're driving up Chapeltown Road, the hookers in small groups trying to sell their wares, large groups of teenage black kids jumping around outside the chicken shop, great big Victorian houses made into flats and bedsits looming over us.

Dustbins burning, surrounded by tramps.

Scary place.

'It's getting bad around here, Gaz. Look at the state of it.'

Steve hates Chapeltown. Doesn't much care for the blacks unless they're doing business with us.

'I've seen worse,' I whisper, whilst staring at the run-down parade of shops from my passenger window.

Steve looks amazed. 'You've seen fucking *worse*? *Where*?'

We both burst out laughing.

'You know what my worst nightmare is, Steve?'

'No. What?'

I go silent for about ten seconds to wind him up.

'I said, do you know what my worst nightmare is?'

Steve looks at me sideways, somewhat disgruntled, and groans, 'Go on, what's your worst nightmare.'

I go silent again, looking out the windows and acting like I haven't heard him.

'Do you know what my worst nightmare is, Steve? Steve. Do you?'

I love winding people up.

He's mad now.

'Fuck off, Gaz. I don't want to know what your worst fucking nightmare fucking is. Fuck off.'

'Go on, have a guess what it is.'

'No, fuck off.'

I sing it to him now in an operatic voice, 'Guess what it is, go on, see if you can. You tit.'

He just stares at me, twitching his eye.

'My worst nightmare is…' I start laughing because his face is getting red with anger, 'is getting kicked to death.'

Steve draws his breath. 'Aw, man, that *would* be shit.'

I carry on, still half giggling, 'I'm not bothered about dying, I just don't want to get kicked to death. I know that everyone, and I mean every single bloke in the land, gets at least one bad kicking during his life, but I don't want to get kicked to death. Especially if they do it from the legs upwards. That *would* be shit. Not even funny.'

Steve's laughing again.

'It happened to me ages ago.' He says this so matter of factly that it's unreal.

I crack up laughing at this statement.

'How the fuck can it have happened to you ages ago? You're not dead, you clown.'

He gets a bit defensive.

'I don't mean kicked to death, you nutter, I mean I took a good kicking. I was seeing this bird, married she was. Anyway, I'm bang at it with her in the bedroom, fucking porno star I was, when we heard her husband come in downstairs and he had three of his mates with him, didn't he? So I've leapt up to the window, bollock naked, and jumped out. Only twisted me fucking ankle, didn't I? That was it, man. All four of 'em ran out, me lying there in the bastard snow, bollocko, and they started to boot the fuck out of me. They even kicked me in me hard on. Can you believe that? I still had a fucking hard on. Not for long though, after they kicked the bastard. Anyway, I didn't die.'

'Fuck that, Stevie boy, getting kicked in the cock is not funny. At all. Anyway, c'mon, we're here.'

Now, pulling up outside the blues, which is only a house with beer and music, is an ordeal in itself – the slags come up and offer you a fifteen quid shag and the little crack heads offer to sell you some rocks. We just tell them all to get fucked.

There are normally a couple of black meatheads on the door. We know 'em usually, but tonight we don't recognise them at all. Two real mean looking bastards. And they've got a dog. A big fuck off pit-bull trying to tear itself away from its master's grip. Slavering and barking like a scary fucking monster.

Boombastic by Shaggy is bellowing through the doorway and out onto the street.

'Not tonight, gents.' The guy who says this looks like Mike Tyson. He even has the crazy shaving on his hair, and he smiles when he says it. No, not a smile, a smirk.

Steve just stares blankly at the floor as I pipe up in my most jovial of voices, 'It's alright, fellas, we've come to meet Rasta Bill, he's got some money for us.'

The sound of my voice is making the dog even madder it seems. It's trying to jump up at me, barking and growling whilst Tyson yanks it back away as forcefully as is possible with such a powerful beast on his wrist.

'I *said*, not to-fuckin'-night. No white bwoys allowed.'

What happened next was a real horror movie situation; in fact when I look back, I'm sure it all happened in black and white. Tyson had hardly finished his sentence when Steve looked up at him with blank eyes and a little grin and said:

'Are you havin' a nice time?'

Then pulled a great big machete from his coat – must have been two foot long – swung it and chopped the dog's fucking head off. Not clean off, mind, just half its head. Tyson and his mate dived back through the doorway screaming, covered in dog blood and brain, slammed the door shut, and I shot back to the car at the bottom of the path, hoping that Steve was following. The garden area was full of people who up until that point had been singing and dancing and whooping and drinking and drugging. Not now. No, now they were all stood still, frozen for just a moment in disbelief at the craziness that was Steve.

I'm shaking like a bastard as I jump into the car, only to look up the path to see Steve lunging at anyone within striking distance, screaming like a maniac, 'I'll fucking kill you all, you bastards.'

It was pandemonium – people running everywhere, girls screaming, *men* screaming. It was like a fire in a Chinese firework factory, reggae music still booming and a great mammoth of a dog lying lifeless. With half a head.

'Steve, c'mon, we've gotta nash. C'mon, the fucking feds'll be here soon.'

Nobody in that place, and I mean nobody, is daft enough to even attempt to chase him down the path.

He's covered in blood as he dives into the motor, and we speed off into the darkest streets of Chapeltown with some hardcore rock music screaming from the stereo.

'Man…' Steve's voice is calm and cool, 'that was pretty hairy.'

I'm still shaking. 'Pretty *hairy*? Steve man, what the fuck were you thinking?'

'Fuck 'em…' He spits, then his manner stops being cool and goes back to the freakshow that I'd just witnessed seconds earlier.

'Fuck them black cunts and fuck their fucking, stupid, fucking, dead, fucking dog. This is *not* Monday night at Tiffany's. They won't fucking bully me.'

I try to lighten his mood a little.

'How many times did you just say fucking then?'

He turns and smiles, and once again we burst out laughing.

You had to admire him.

But he scared me that night.

I often wondered if it was Bill the Rasta who had set us up that night, put the two guys on the door so that he wouldn't have to pay us our money. I'd never find out though; Bill was found two weeks later, slumped over his steering wheel at the side of the canal, a single bullet wound through his eye.

Nobody ever found out who did it. Another unsolved killing for the cops to add to their list.

Like I said, beware the little guy.

CHAPTER THREE

—

BOOT POLISH AND PARANOIA

Empire State Human– Phil Oakey,
Human League, 1979

AUTUMN 1982– AGED 15

When you're fifteen, all you want to do is either go out and get drunk with your mates, or go out and get drunk with your mates and get a girl. Neither choice a bad one, I'm sure you'll agree.

Saturdays were beautiful: no school, of course, *and* we could stay out later than weeknights. Yes, Saturdays were beautiful.

The afternoon would usually be spent roaming around the city centre looking for girls. Hanging outside the record shops, where the punks would be cutting their hair with penknives and the mods would be peacocking in front of the plate glass windows.

Our success with women was somewhat erratic at this time. Oh sure, they fancied us and that was great. But we didn't want to be fancied, we wanted to *shag*.

But apart from a couple of not very inspiring attempts at doing the dirty, I hadn't had much in the way of action, if you know what I mean.

We were gagging. Exploding even.

We were fifteen.

There was me and there was Mel. His real name was Shaun but we called him Mel. There was Ricko. His name was really John but we called him Ricko. And there was Mark. His name really was Mark.

We were all the same age except for Mark, who was a couple of years younger than us. We didn't mind him hanging around with us because he had a sister who we all wanted to shag. She wasn't super fit or anything, we just wanted to shag her. We wanted to shag anyone.

Except fat birds.

I never could see the appeal of fat birds. I know some guys who actively seek them out, but no, not for me I'm afraid.

Mel liked fat birds.

'What's wrong with you, Gaz, you can't be choosy y'know.'

'I'm not choosy, fuckin'ell, look at some of the states I keep getting off with. I just don't get off on fatties. You know my rule, man –if I can't lift 'em above me head, they're not coming in me bed.'

'Well, I *love* 'em…' Mel started to lick his lips as he proceeded to make voluptuous curve shapes with his hands, gyrating his pelvis. 'I love 'em because when you shag a fat bird…' he's thrusting back and forth now, 'when you shag a fat bird, she thinks it's the last shag she's ever gonna get, man. She'll go like the clappers.'

'Fuck off, man. How do you know that? You've never shagged *anyone*, let alone a fat bird.'

I chuckled as I announced this, smirking at Ricko and giving him a sly wink.

Ricko started laughing.

'So what? I might not have shagged anyone yet, but our kid has and he told me. He's shagged loads of birds, fat ones and everything.'

Mel did have an older brother, about twenty he was, and he did always have girls with him. It might have been true.

These were the kinds of things we always talked about when we were getting ready to go to the church disco on a Saturday night. The Immaculate Heart of Mary disco. The Maccy Heart, as we called it. It was the bollocks, man. Not as glamorous as Tiffany's of course, it was only in a church hall, but it was cool enough all the same.

A hundred and fifty kids, a fair mix of lads and lasses, all similar ages and looking to "get off" with each other.

We'd get ready at my house. I always had everyone at my house. Putting our nice threads on, black and purple boating blazer with the gold buttons no less, Fred Perry shirt and two-tone trousers, black loafers, and don't forget to gel the hair. You had to gel the hair. We'd have the Ramones and The Jam on the stereo, and we'd be drinking cider from the Paki shop. Just to get us nicely before we got there. Only soft drinks inside the Maccy Heart. Paff.

We were never the biggest lads around, nor were we the hardest, yet we still always walked about as though each of us were Nine Foot Tall, as though we were ten men. We thought we were *the* men.

We had all perfected this pronounced swagger when we walked. We'd seen John Travolta doing it in *Grease* a couple of years previously, and we thought it was the coolest. We entered any place we went as though we were going up to collect an award. The other guys often let slip, y'know, they came out of character now and again. It became second nature to me though. Even to this day.

Hey, why walk when you can STRUT.

We used to play-fight, watch Bruce Lee films and then do kung fu on each other, never hurting each other, just messing, y'know. Our unsaid and unwritten rule was that we're all equally as hard. But we knew, we all knew, that Ricko, should it come to it, that Ricko was "top boy".

I felt sorry for Ricko, not just because he had a mad haircut that was really long at the back and short on top. His dad had died a year ago, and his brother was on his way to becoming a junkie – he was funny though. He used to get us weed.

We'd drink our cider and have a joint and then we'd be off, off to the Maccy Heart.

To pull.

Inside was no great shakes. A DJ at the front with a few shitty flashing lights and a smoke machine. A row of wooden chairs down either side of the room and a rickety old wallpaper paste table where the plastic cups full of diluted orange were being sold by one of the church helpers. You know the sort, the old women who make coffee for the priest on a Sunday morning.

And that was it.

But we still loved it.

All the latest music, The Specials and Kraftwerk and Bananarama. The girls would line up down one side of the room and the boys down the other for the first hour of the night. Then after a few more sneaky ciders or another shared joint, they'd all get more daring and start dancing in groups. Same sex groups of course, it was only early.

Cannabis has never liked me. I've never liked it, either. It's always done "funny" things to me. I'd still smoke it though, just to be part of the gang.

So, we're huddled in a small group, steaming drunk from the cheap cider and the couple of swallows of blow that we've been sneaking outside for now and again. The lights are swirling, as is the whole room, smoke billowing from the crappy machine, and there's a gang of girls looking right at us. Right at *us*.

I'm slumped in my chair as one of them approaches me, fit as shit she is as well. Could be my lucky night.

'My mate fancies you.' She giggles as she tells me.

Aw fuck. I knew it was too good to be true. Here she is, fit as fuck, and it's her mate who fancies me.

'Yeah? Which mate?' I look over and all I can see is about seven or eight big fat birds dancing round a tiny white handbag.

'The one with the miniskirt. She's been looking at you for ages and she daren't come over.'

Of all the luck, the only fit bird in the place doesn't want to know. But her fat mate does.

Oh well, fuck it.

All I can hear in my head, besides throbbing from the cider and weed, is Mel's brother: 'Fat birds go like the clappers…go like the clappers…go like the clappers.'

Come to think of it, in the state I was in she didn't look bad at all. Fat, yes, little miniskirt hugging her big fat thighs, yes. But not bad all the same. Pretty face, as they always say.

I might as well fill me boots.

'Send her over. I'll see what I can do.' I thought I was John Travolta, cool as ice.

Fit bird hurried back and told her friend. Before I knew it there she was, towering over me as I lay out on my chair. She was even bigger close up. Fifteen stone easy. Scary.

Her mates weren't much better, except for the fit one of course.

Now, in those days, I don't know if this still happens, but then, you wouldn't have to chat the girls up, nope, you would just start kissing them, necking. This was us, slobbering like a couple of pigs, my mates all laughing and all.

Before I knew it we were outside. There was a great big weeping willow tree around the back where everybody always went to… well… y'know.

I'm gonna get me nuts. This is ace. I'm under the shagging tree and I'm gonna get me nuts.

With a big fat bird.

Still slobbering like boxer dogs, I haven't even felt her tits when…

'What the fuck you doing with our mate? You little cunt. She's only thirteen.'

These girls were big, fat as fuck, man. All her mates standing outside the weeping branches of the shagging tree and they're shouting in to me as though they mean business.

Pretty Face Fatty has passed out under me, pissed out of her bleedin' head. Fuckin' thirteen? Yeah right, thirteen stone maybe. At a push.

'I didn't know she was only thirteen!' I shout through the branches. 'We haven't done anything anyway, we were only kissing.'

They don't seem to want to listen.

'Get the fuckin' perv.' And they dive through the branches like mad animals.

I'm not hanging around to get kicked to death by a gang of birds. A gang of fat birds.

I'm up and I'm off, darting around like a whippet. They won't catch me, they're too fat.

I run back into the disco and shout the others, but these fat fuckers don't care, they'll chin us all.

Now, unbeknown to us, these fat 'uns were in with their brothers as well.

Aw for fuck's sake.

Not only have we got the bitches from hell chasing us down the road but their equally mad and equally large brothers are now on our case as well.

Gasping and nearly out of breath, running faster than our legs can go, me, Mel, Mark and Ricko, running for our lives.

Hang on a sec, strike that. No Ricko.

'Where's Ricko?' I'm flapping now as I shout to the other two who are just in front of me.

Mel shouts, 'Fuck knows, he must have got away, down a side street or summat.'

I look behind and I can't see anyone. Looks like they've given up the chase.

We sneak up a few side roads to make sure we're out of sight altogether and head home. Without Ricko. Good, I'm glad he got away. I mean, it was me they were after really, they thought I was a perv.

As we got back to our own estate that night, Ricko was sitting on my garden step with his head in his hands.

'Yo, Ricko man. You got away.' I'm relieved for him.

He looks up at me and my heart sinks. His face is battered and bruised, black eyes and swollen mouth.

'They were kickin' me in the fuckin' mouth. The cunts. I can taste fuckin' boot polish off their Doc Martens on me teeth.'

And he was right. Upon closer inspection, not only was there dried blood in his gob but he had black boot polish all over his teeth.

We all killed ourselves laughing, even Ricko. He called us cunts, but he still laughed as we helped him get home.

To think, I nearly shagged a fat bird.

I told you weed did funny things to me.

Saturdays were beautiful.

JUNE 1996 – AGED 29

They say that one person in every thousand has psychopathic tendencies. This, I do not believe. It seems that every *other* person I meet is in some way a pathological freak.

Mad Marko was one of those people.

Mad Marko lived in an old 1960s tower block, one of those rat-infested, piss-smelling monstrosities that are still blighting the skyline of the ever-growing metropolis that is Leeds.

He lived alone, apart from the fungus on the back of his toilet door, and his sole purpose on this planet, it would seem, was to be cabbaged out of his fragile, tiny mind every night.

Oh, and to buy and sell drugs. Any drugs.

The stories go that Mad Marko had been sectioned under the Mental Health Act on more than one occasion. The last time, apparently, he was found sitting astride the statue of the horse in Leeds City Square, singing Christmas carols. Naked. During the day. And it was June.

They say he's had electric shock treatment.

Do they really do that in those places? I suspect not.

Whatever the case, he is one big, bald, mean, unhinged, Honey Monster looking, scary motherfucker.

And I had to go and visit him. Shit.

I didn't know where to get rid of morphine. Fuck no. All I did was sell a bit of whizz and a couple of Es. But I was skint. I had some hospital morphine that they give to cancer patients, and I wanted to offload it.

I'd tried to get rid of it in the local pubs, but nobody wanted to know.

'We're not fucking smack heads, Gaz,' is all I would get out of them. We hated smack heads.

Heroin addicts. Scum.

Mad Marko knew loads of smack heads. His dingy 10th floor hovel was always full of them, crashed out in his bed, on his sofa, in his bath. In the lift even.

So I called him up.

The deal was this: I go to his flat, the flea-bitten shithole that it is, give him the bag of morphine, and he would do a straight swap for fifty Es.

And the variety of Es were my personal favourite, Ziggys – they had an imprint of the iconic image of David Bowie with the lightning bolt through his face embossed on them. It was a bit of a misnomer to be fair, as that image wasn't Ziggy, it was Aladdin Sane… Well, never mind, they were my E of choice anyway.

Spot on. That would do for me.

'Come round tonight, ya little cunt…' He always called me a little cunt. He appeared to really have a soft spot for me but still called me a little cunt. In a sort of affectionate way. 'Get here about two o'clock after you finish DJing.'

I finished my set that night, a good set too, the place had been rocking. The place could never help but rock when I was playing. I was mashed out of my tree; always played better when I was mullied.

I could hear the music blaring from Marko's gaff, even from the stinking lift.

His door was wide open when I got there and I could see all kinds of nutters around the place as I entered. Girls sitting on the hallway floor, smoking crack pipes, guys crashed out on the kitchen, bathroom and toilet floors. A bedroom door was slightly ajar and I could make out, in the half-light, a bloke lying face down on the bed, long matted hair at the back. I kind of recognised him, didn't know where from though. Fuck him. Smack head.

'Come in here, you little cunt.' Marko sounded really jolly as he shouted me into his arsehole of a living room.

It was full of smoke, quite dark, just a crappy forty watt lamp and the orange light from his one-bar electric fire.

There were about ten people in that room. A couple of haggard looking girls, obviously E'd up by the way they were dancing and contorting their faces. You could tell that once upon a time these girls had been really pretty. Not now. Twenty-eight going on fifty. All sunken cheeks and leathered sun bed skin. Hair bleached to lifelessness.

The Mad One himself was sitting in the middle of his velvet sofa drinking lager out of a vase, and there were a few young guys around him, talking about fighting and glassing fuckers in the neck and shit like that. Trying to impress him I expect.

Let me get the fuck out of here. Do my swap and fuck off.

'Sit down, you little cunt, grab a drink.' He pointed to some cans on his sideboard.

'I'll just have one, man,' I mumble, 'I'm a bit mashed. Can't stay long. Here's that stuff you wanted.' I chuck him the carrier bag full of morph, he catches it in one hand and, as if from nowhere, by magic, his other hand throws me my Es.

'Don't eat 'em all at once. You little cunt.' He booms with laughter at this comment and is then followed in his merriment by everyone else in the room. The hangers-on.

I'm looking nervous and twitchy. I fuckin' hate this place.

'Sit down, Gaz...' He *never* calls me Gaz, something's wrong. 'Sit down, have a beer and chill out.'

The others are looking at me, as if, I don't know, as if something bad is gonna happen. I know. It's paranoia. Fuckin'ell, I should have known. I'm relieved now. It's just paranoia.

Es always make me paranoid. Now that I *know* it's paranoia, I can chill out.

I try to make some conversation.

'So, Marko, what are you gonna do with that morphine? You're gonna take it yourself, are you?'

He stares at me. Right in my eye. As though I'd just called his mother a bastard.

'Fuck off, you little cunt. I'm no *smack head*. It's for him in there, on the bed. Richardson.'

'Richardson? Do I know him?' I ask, hoping he'll calm the fuck down.

Still staring in my eye he shouts, 'How the fuck do I know if you know him?! John Richardson. Smack head, that's all. He's just a fucking smack head.'

I knew at that point where I recognised the body on the bed from. It was Ricko. My old friend Ricko. Aw shit, man, he's a smack head.

I did hear that his mother had died soon after his dad, and then, when we all grew up and grew apart, that his brother, who we used to get weed off, had thrown himself from a train. Got cut in half.

Fuckin 'hell, Gaz, poor Ricko's a smack head and you've brought him some drugs.

I'm having a little reminisce to myself, staring out of Marko's 10th-floor window at the night sky, what a great view, when...

Mad Marko lunges at me, and in a split second he has the window open and he's pushed me right out of it, grabbing my legs so I don't fall to my certain death.

I'm screaming like a woman, him holding me by my ankles, dangling ten floors up, piss-stained concrete below. He's gonna let me go. I know he is. I'm screaming, please, please, please.

I can hear the hangers-on through the window laughing their spines out. Oh, they think it's hilarious.

'Shut up screaming, you little cunt, or I'll let you go...' He shakes me about a little as though he's gonna drop me. I'm not struggling, fuck that, I'll fall. 'Right, here's what's gonna happen. That bag you just gave me is mine, right?'

I look up at him and nod furiously.

'And… and… that bag I gave *you* is mine as well. Innit?'

Fuck! Is this what it's about? He wants to rip me off? I don't care, I got the morphine for free, and if he's not gonna drop me on my head from ten floors up he can keep the fuckin' Es. Especially now that all the blood in my entire body has rushed to my head and it feels four times bigger than it should.

'Fuck yes, keep it, keep the fuckin' lot… Just get me back inside. You're gonna drop me, you crazy cunt.'

He shakes me about a little more, swapping hands and all that crazy shit. I scream. A lot.

And he pulls me back in. Laughing.

I'm as white as… I don't what the fuckin' whitest thing ever is, but whatever it is I'm as white as that.

'I was only messing, Gaz…' He's still laughing. 'I wouldn't let you fall. I like you. Keep the drugs, I was only playing.'

'Playing?' I try to get my breath. 'Fuckin' playin'? You could have dropped me.'

Everyone in the room is killing themselves with laughter.

I shake my head in disbelief, grab my bag of Es and go. Fast.

I don't even peep in to see my old friend Ricko, to see if he's alright with these lunatics. I just fuck off. To an all-night club. With my bag of Ziggys.

I never saw Mad Marko after that.

They say he got sectioned again.

Good. The mad cunt.

I did hear about Ricko though. He overdosed apparently.

Some bastard had given him hospital-strength morphine. It was too much for him.

And he died.

CHAPTER FOUR

—

FISH, CHIPS AND POTATO PEELERS

I Fought The Law–The Clash –1979
(written by Sonny Curtis)

JULY 1983 — AGED 16

Breaking up for the summer was the highlight of the year, but this year would be different for us. It would be the highlight of our lives – we were breaking up forever. Leaving school. We were now sixteen. We were *men*.

The summer holidays were the greatest. It was always sunny and you always had fun. Even when you were skint.

Sure, I had a little job on a Sunday night, collecting glasses at a local pub, but we never had lots of cash. Just enough to get by, y'know, bus fare into town and that.

We didn't care. We didn't need money.

We just had fun.

So, here I am, it's the holidays, the sun is beating down across the estate where we live, shining onto the windows of the flats, the ones that aren't boarded up, and all is sweet.

My mam's made me some bacon and eggs, KC and The Sunshine Band are jumping out of the kitchen radio singing *Give it Up*.

'Gaz…!' My mam shouted from the lounge, over the sound of the vacuum cleaner. I could never understand that, mams trying to get your attention while the vac's going and the radio's blaring. But it's what they do I suppose. 'Will you do me a favour when you go in town with your mates?'

Mouthful of bacon, packed in so I can't even chew it properly. 'Yeh, course I will. What do you want?'

'Will you go to the water board and pay the bill for me? I'll give you the book. All you have to do is give the woman the money and get the book stamped. It'll only take you a minute.'

'I'm sure I can manage that, love, no problem. Can I have a couple of quid for some chips? I've only got me bus fare.'

She switched off the vac, thank fuck, smiled at me, gave me a kiss on the top of the head and passed me the water payment book and a five-pound note. That's two quid for me and three for the water board people.

I didn't even know that you had to pay for water.

So, there's me, Mel and Ricko all going into town. Mark couldn't come; he was younger than us so hadn't broken up from school yet. We broke up earlier than the younger ones, took our exams and… well, just broke up earlier. I don't know why.

We're in town, doing what we do best – strutting.

First port of call? HMV.

Yes, the record shop. Always a good place to pull a bird.

In the early '80s the record shop was a meeting place, like a little club or something, always full of gangs of girls, and it was free entry. Ace.

Baby Jane was playing when we walked in. Cool. Rod Stewart was a bit of an old-timer. But the girls loved it when he was singing. Good old Rod, he made it easier for us to pull.

So, we're strutting up and down the aisles, racks of vinyl albums, millions of them, trying to catch the eye of some of the many beauties who are flicking through the Paul Young section, when…

'Gaz! Mel! Ricko!' We heard some goon shouting at us.

Aw no. Not him. Fuck sake.

It was Psycho. Sykesey was his real name, but he was nuts, always fighting and shit. And he was an *Ugly Fucker*. A face that even a dog wouldn't lick. One eye higher than the other, tongue too big for his mouth and two cauliflower ears. Not one. Two. You had no chance of getting a bird with him around.

'Alright, girls…' He thought he was a funny fucker calling us girls. He was just jealous of our good looks. 'What yuz doin'?'

'We were just off, man…' I said this so we could get rid of him. Y'know, fuck off and come back later when he's gone. 'We've gotta go pay me mam's water rates, nowt special.'

A big smile comes over his stupid looking big-tongued face.

'Aw that's *ace*! I thought I was gonna be on me lonesome all day. I'll come wi' ya.'

Not one of us wanted him with us. It'd end in tears, always does with him around.

'Nah, man, it'll be boring, Psycho. What do ya wanna come there for? We'll go pay the thing and then come back 'ere and meet you.' We all nod at each other, mumbling 'yeh' and 'sound'.

He's determined to come, though.

'Nope. I've made me mind up, I'm coming wi' ya. I've been in here two hours and all they keep playing is Rod fucking Stewart, doing me head in, man. And everyone keeps staring at me face as well. What's wrong with 'em, don't they fancy me?'

He strokes his cauliflower ear and licks his lips with his giant fat tongue and laughs. Like a nutter.

We are not happy. At all. We're gonna be lumbered with him now, all fucking day.

It's not as bad as it had first seemed. We're strutting down to the water board and all is good. Psycho is in quite a good mood, making us laugh and telling funny stories and stuff. Maybe he's not so bad after all, he just wants to hang about with some mates.

Now, the inside of the water board is a little like a bank to look at. Y'know, windows with women behind them, taking your payments from under a little space at the bottom of the glass.

Today there's only one woman working and there are two people in front of me waiting to pay for their water. The boys are hanging around at the end of the counter, waiting for me to pay the thing. They're being a bit boisterous, as you do.

The woman keeps looking at them as if they are scum. They're only messing, what's wrong with her? She looks a bit like Miss Jean Brodie, all school ma'amish or nun like.

My turn.

I pass the book under the glass and, 'Can I pay me mam's water please, missus?'

She just nods, all the while glancing sideways at my mates. She takes my money, stamps the book and shouts, 'Next!'

Fucking charming. No thank you or fuck all. The miserable old bastard.

As I walk to leave the building, the guys walk out in front of me and down the great stone steps that lead up to the revolving doors. I can see Psycho looking really shifty as we walk down the steps.

'What the fuck's up with him?' I ask Ricko.

'He's got the money, c'mon.' Ricko starts to run. Then Psycho and then Mel. *'C'MON!'* he shouts behind to me, stood on me own like a lemon.

'What money?' I shout after them.

Then, as if by magic, The Miserable Prime of Miss Jean Brodie runs through the revolving doors and screams from the top of the steps, *'Stop! Thieves!'*

Fuck this, I'm off. Like a *Bat Out of Hell* is playing in my head. Running like a speeding bullet.

Almost up to the others now, they're shouting for me to catch up, we're down alleys, up side streets, through car parks and then... Stop.

'We're safe. C'mon, let's stop for a bit.' Psycho's panting and grunting as he says this and plonks himself on the grass verge.

I'm delirious as to what has even happened. Haven't got a clue.

The others are all laughing and jumping about, linking arms and singing, 'We're in the money!'

'What fucking money?' I still haven't got the faintest idea what's gone on.

Psycho, sitting with his legs crossed on the grass, pulls a big wad of cash out of his pocket, big enough to choke a pig, and says, 'This fucking money! There must be ten grand here, boys.'

I'm curious now.

'Where... where the fuck did you get that lot?'

Psycho piped up, with a huge retarded grin, 'In there, man, that water place. It was easy, Gaz. It was just lying there, under the end window, waiting to be plucked away. I just stuck me arm under the glass... and took the fucker. Fuck that woman, man, she's long gone. She's gone and we're rich!'

That was it then. We all jumped and sang and hugged and kissed and sang again. We were rich.

It was all in fivers, so it looked as though there was more than there really was, but after counting it up there was five hundred. Five hundred fucking quid. Three months' wages in the '80s, and that's grown-up wages – I only got five quid a week glass-collecting.

God bless Psycho and his great big tongue, he shared it out equally, a hundred and twenty-five each, all in five-pound notes.

To think, this morning I only had enough for my bus fare and some chips. This money would last me till I was twenty. At least.

We walked around town wondering what to buy, how to spend our loot – clothes, records, shoes. We could get anything we wanted.

We were starving after all that running so went to the chip shop. Fish and chips… four times.

And that's just about all we bought, except for me. I also bought a silver skull and crossbones earring. Cool. Big dangly thing it was. A quid twenty-five. It wasn't real silver.

We were so excited that we agreed not to impulse buy, that we'd go home, hide the money and then go to Blackpool for a few days.

I was wearing leg-hugging, stretch-denim jeans that day, Smart R's. I stuffed my wad of dough into the super skin-tight pocket and headed home. Head spinning. I'm rich. I'm rich.

It was late afternoon as I walked down the street to my house, still lovely and sunny, all the young 'uns playing tennis in the street because Wimbledon was on. Funny that, kids only like to play tennis at Wimbledon time.

My plan was this: open the front door really quietly, sneak in and go upstairs to my room to hide the money. No problem.

I get to my house, quietly turn the handle and open the door, when…

'Gaz…!' It was my mam calling from the lounge. 'Get in here now.'

I tried to walk to the staircase.

'Two minutes, Mam, I'm just nipping to the bog.'

'*NOW!*' she shouted. Something was wrong. She never shouted unless the vacuum cleaner and the radio were on at the same time.

I looked sheepishly around the lounge door frame. Aw fuck.

There's my mam, my dad and two big fuckers. Two big fuckers with suits and ties on.

They weren't smiling either. Not one of them.

The first big fucker opened his mouth, 'Hello Gaz, how are you?'

I'm shitting in my pants almost.

'Erm, I'm cush thanks.'

'Good. I'm glad you're cush.' He stared right at me as he spoke, watching for… well, I don't know what he was watching for but he was still staring. 'Where's the money, Gaz?'

I don't believe it, he came straight out with it – how does he know? We only got it two hours ago. I know, I can blag it, just deny everything and he can't do a thing.

'What money?' I say this as calmly as I can to avoid detection, but it just comes over as cocky to the adults.

My dad pipes up, 'Gaz, these two fellas are policemen, CID, so don't lie to them. Tell the truth and it'll be better for you.'

CID. Cunts In Disguise, Mel's brother called them. I don't need this shit.

I carry on denying it for a few minutes – I don't know what you're talking about and all that rubbish, when…

'Okay, then, Gaz…' the other big fucker smiles at me, 'how much money have you got on you?'

'Erm, er, nothing, nowt. I only had two quid that me mam gave me for some chips and I've spent it. I ain't got owt.'

They are all staring at my jeans, Mam, Dad, two fat coppers, all looking at my Smart R's.

'Empty your pockets please, Gaz.' He's still smiling, the clever fucker.

I know I've been busted now. Nothing I can do to get away with it, just play for time.

Back pocket first: a door key... slam... on the table.

Other back pocket: penknife and Polo mints... bang...table.

Front pocket: they are all looking with eager anticipation... two bus tickets... bang... table.

'And that pocket, Gazzy baby, the one with the great big giant bulge in it. What's in there?'

He's still smiling. He knows full well what's in there. The bastard. He's just making me sweat. In front of my mam and dad.

I pull out the wad of notes and drop it on the table. My mam and dad both put their heads in their hands.

And the cops give me all the under arrest shit and cuff me up.

Fuckin' stupid tight jeans.

I wouldn't tell them who I'd been out with that day.

But my mam did.

Mel's mam never said anything, but Ricko's mam said it must have been my fault, I'm a bad influence. Fuck, I didn't even know till it was too late.

Stupid fucking Sykesey. Psycho. With his funny face and his massive tongue. Going and robbing a place where I'd just given them a book with my bastard address on. Dur!

Because we'd only spent some money for fish and chips, the water board got most of their money back, so the courts didn't go as harsh as they could have done.

They didn't even mention the fake silver skull and crossbones earring.

Instead of Robbery, which could have got us four years in a young offenders institute, where we would most definitely have got arse raped every day, we got Handling.

Handling Stolen Goods. Forty quid fine and a stern telling off. Not bad at all, my son.

Smelling of roses comes to mind.

Breaking up for the summer was the highlight of the year.

JULY 1996 – AGED 29

Once you've seen somebody get really fucked up, kicked in the head, without mercy, over and over and over. When you see that black blood coming from their ears. When you know that you've seen someone get fucked up so bad that they're never gonna recover, and if they do they'll be eating through a plastic pipe for the rest of their lives. Once you've seen that, that day will stick in your head forever. Forever.

Today was that day.

Sunday was usually a good day for me. A good day for business that is.

On the seventh day, the Lord rested.

On the seventh day, Gaz and Unsolved Steve went out and took copious amounts of drugs, and made some easy cash.

'The Mass is ended. Go in peace to love and serve the Lord.'

It had been at least thirteen years since I'd heard these words uttered – for some, the *only* words that were heard throughout the whole of Mass.

But something had compelled me to go to Mass today. Don't know what it was, I just knew I had to go.

It made me feel good too, an enormous sense of well-being. That and the drugs I'd taken only a couple of hours earlier.

It still felt good, it felt good because I'd chosen to go, of my own accord. Not like when I was younger. When I was younger I was *made* to go. With my little sister. Yuk.

My dad sometimes came with us, but if he didn't he would tell us to go, and just so we wouldn't sneak off to the park with our mates he would tell us to bring back a Mass sheet and explain to him what the gospel had centred on.

Today's gospel spoke of Jesus mixing with tax collectors and sinners (Matthew 9.9-13).

Anyway, I've done my bit for Catholicism today. It's time to go meet Steve.

Sunday to us was usually an extension of Saturday, which in turn was an extension of Friday.

It went like this.

Friday morning, meet Steve and go to the pub for opening time. Drink beer and brandy and eat lots of chemicals up to closing time. Go to an all-night club. Drink and chemicals. Go to some strange house for an after party, complete stranger's house most of the time, but who cares? More drink, more chemicals. By this time it would be Saturday morning. Go to a cafe for some eggs and bacon. Back to the pub for opening and through to Sunday morning, more breakfast then straight to the pub again. We had our chemical assistance to beat the sleep. Es, coke and a big bag of Billy.

And that's what Sunday would consist of, mucho Billy-o. Had to be alert.

Everyone had been out all weekend, all feeling jaded, and would come to us for their pick-me-ups. Paid for our beer money and more drugs, if nothing else.

One of our favourite haunts on a Sunday was an all-day drinking den by the name of Flanagan's. It sounds like it should be an Irish bar. It's not. It's a shithole. The only thing Irish about the gaff is the little shamrock on the sign outside and the fifty or so pikeys who would congregate there. Not a hint of Irish music, unless the pikeys started to sing in the beer garden, which was quite often. They'd sing, then they'd fight. Each other. For fun. They used to fight each other for *fun*.

But we got on well with the pikeys, the travellers. They loved their beer and chemicals.

That meant they loved us. We had the chemicals.

We drove up to Flanagan's in Steve's car that day, a lovely, lovely BMW. Private number plate too, D34 LER.

As we drove up past the canal, I saw, in the distance, someone throw a dog into the canal.

'Fuckin'ell, Steve man. Did ya see that? Some cunt just chucked a dog off at bridge. Into the canal. Fuck me, man. I don't believe what I just saw, the cruel bastard. How can people do things like that, Steve man? It's beyond me. Have you ever hurt an animal?'

Steve thought for a moment, then said, 'What? On purpose or by accident?'

'Any. Either. Why? Have you? Have you hurt summat? You have, 'ant yer?'

'Yeh, then. Yeh I 'ave. I killed an elephant once.'

I nearly choked on my cigarette smoke.

'A fuckin' *elephant*?'

He seems to have completely forgotten chopping off a dog's head last year. But I suppose that's allowed though, it being a bouncer's dog, trying to bite us and that.

'Yeh, man. A baby elephant. Killed it stone dead.'

I laugh out loud. I can't believe what I'm hearing.

'How the fuck did you kill an elephant? There aren't any elephants round 'ere, man. Where did you even *see* an elephant? Let alone kill one.'

'I went to India, Gaz man, Goa…' He doesn't find this quite as amusing as I do. He's telling me his story with the straightest face I have ever seen. Ever. 'Yeh, Goa. It was cush. Nice place, red hot too. Anyway, I hired this motorbike for a day, big fuck off thing it was, a right beast, fast as fuck. I'm teararsing round the countryside at about eighty mile an hour, flew round a corner and crashed into an elephant. Killed it, man. Dead.'

I'm still laughing.

'So you just banged into a baby elephant, then? And it died? Fuck off, man. You're bullshitting me. A wild elephant? Just walking around?'

'Yeh, man. It's true. Out there, man, in Goa, stuff just walks about, free like. Not like here where it's all in a zoo and that. I flew round a corner and smashed into a baby elephant. It wasn't massive, it were only about four foot high. Fat little fucker though. Nearly broke me bike. It just fell over when I crashed into it, then it grunted, then it died. All these Indian geezers were jumpin' around shouting and wavin' their fists at me. So I got back on me bike and fucked off. I saw all sorts of stuff there, man. Huge cows with big curly horns. Big flying things and all sorts. It were mad.'

'What do you mean? Big flying things? What sort of fuckin' things?' I'm astonished.

'I don't know, Gaz man, just massive stuff what flies.'

'Eh? Massive *stuff*? What kind of stuff? Birds? Insects? What?'

'Gaz man. Just stuff. I don't what they were. Just animals or summat.'

'*Animals*? Fuckin' *animals*? Well fuck that, Stevie boy, I'm not *ever* gonna go to no India. That's for sure. Flying *stuff*? Flying *animals*? Fuck that. You're crackers, man, going to mad places like that. I wish I'd never asked you anything in the first place. I'm gonna have nightmares, man. Flying *stuff*? Fuck me.'

It still amazes me, the shite that comes out of people's mouths when they're off their heads. All I could think about for the next few minutes was flying animals. What were they? Perhaps they were like the Screaming Devil Monkeys from *The Wizard of Oz*. But in India. Not the Magical Land of Oz.

'Don't you just love the red hot, sunny, sexy summertime, Gaz?'

Steve was extra giddy and happy today. The sun shining, the pocket full of cash. The whizz and Charlie in his brain.

'I do, man, I do…' I was giddy too, in a playful mood. Time to wind him up a little. 'Steve man… what's wi' that *stupid* number plate, for fuck sake?'

'Whatyonnabout? It's *ace*.' He nods his head furiously in time to the tune on his radio.

'Ace? Steve man, it's not ace. It's gonna get us nicked. Every cop who drives past is gonna stop us. Every single one. All day, every day. Stop. Search. Stop. Search. Nicked. Nicked. Nicked.'

Winding up Steve is so easy.

'What you trying to say, Gaz? That my number plate's crap?'

'Yeh I am. It's crap. C.R.A.P. All private plates are crap. It's like having stone cladding on yer house. But crapper. Yours is even crapper than anyone else's coz it says *DEALER* and it's gonna get you nicked. Me too if I'm wi' yer. If it dunt get yer nicked it'll at least get yer loads of hassle. Fuckin' *DEALER*. It's crap. Rubbish.'

'Well, I like it. If the feds stop me I'll tell 'em to get fucked. How's that grab yer?'

He means it too, he would, he'd tell the cops to get fucked.

I carry on with my little party game.

'And that *fuckin'* chain you've got on, well…' Steve wore one of those great, big, fat, ridiculous gold chains around his neck, weighed a ton man. 'With that fuckin' stupid chain on, weighin' yer neck down, yer might as well have a big sign on yer head saying *I AM A DRUG DEALER*. You look like a bastard, man. Big silly chain and crappy number plate.'

I can't help laughing while I'm saying all this, Steve's laughing too, but he can't tell if I mean it or not, which makes me laugh even more.

'Aw stop it now, Gaz, fuck off. This silly chain cost me three grand and me mam bought me this number plate for me birthday. So stop laughing at it. You see that wire…?' He points to a wire that leads to his mobile phone plug, the in-car charging kit. 'Plug it out for me please.'

I look at him with a puzzled expression.

'Plug it out?'

He puts on some sort of posh upper crust accent. 'Oh yes please, Cedric. Would you mind terribly? I'm concentrating on the road, you see. I need you to plug it out for me.'

'Plug it out? You mean *unplug*. You don't say plug it out. It's not right. Unplug. I'll unplug it for you. Fuckin' plug it out. Ya mad cunt.' I'm shaking my head, chuckling.

'I'll say plug it out if I want. OK?' Ha ha, he's shouting at me now.

Yes, I've done it, I've got him going, his voice is getting mad. I love it when he gets mad, it makes me laugh.

He raises his voice a little more. 'I'll say plug the fucker out coz when I plug the fucker in I say "plug it in". There. That *must* be right then, mustn't it? Plug it in and then plug it out. Yep. Plug it out. Plug it out. Plug the fucker out. My silly gold chain is a nice gold chain, and me mam's birthday present number plate is *not* like bastard stone cladding. Fuckin' stone cladding? What's *that* supposed to mean? I like stone cladding. And it's *plug* it *fuckin' out*. C'mon, you mad little cunt, we're here.'

I'm falling around laughing at his outburst as we get out. He's chuckling too, not the mad belly laughter that I'm convulsed with, he's just chuckling.

Sunny weather, drink and chemicals, lots of laughter. Nothing can go wrong today. Right?

Wrong.

We're walking into the place, through the beer garden, nodding to people, saying hello, alright fella, got some gear, want some gear, how's yer head, how's your lass and all that kind of shite, when we spot them. The Lonnegan brothers. All six of 'em. Aw fuck, not them.

Fuckin' 'ellfire. Not them.

The Lonnegan brothers. The Vicious brothers.

All six of 'em. Crazy, deranged, violent to the extreme. They love jail. How can anyone win against someone who loves jail? They love to fight the blacks, they love to fight the pikeys, and they love to fight the police! If they get into a fight and some fucker calls the law, the Lonnegans wait. Every normal sane person fucks off. Not them. They wait and they have a fight with the police. They are nutters. They're not even from Leeds, man, they're from Hull or somewhere. They just come here to cause trouble.

The last time I saw any of the Lonnegan brothers was here in Flanagan's a few months previously. I was almost asleep in the beer garden one afternoon, the place was packed, rocking it was, when in come two of the Lonnegans, Jimmy and Frankie. They walk straight up to this giant of a man, not a word and *BANG*. Baseball bat around his crust. If that wasn't bad enough, the force of the whack made the bloke's eye pop out. Popped right out of his head. Onto the grass.

It soon made me wake up, seeing that, I can tell you. There were women screaming, the giant guy was screaming, they were all screaming, man. The Lonnegans? They just went inside and ordered some drinks. Like nothing had happened. Crazy fuckers. Crazy fuckers who are here today. All six of 'em.

Jimmy, Frankie, Terry, Gaz, Baz and Finbar.

Jimmy is the eldest, about forty. He's probably the only one out of the lot of them who's really hard. Oh yeah, the rest of them are mad enough, but they're not really hard. If they went toe to toe with some hard nut, they'd lose. But they're mad, so going toe to toe isn't an option; they use weapons and go mob-handed. Jimmy is the one with the reputation really, the rest just want be like him; except for that, he's quite a nice bloke. Unless you upset him. Then he's not nice. Jimmy Lonnegan will go toe to toe with anyone, and he will probably win.

Frankie "I am afraid of no man and there isn't a dog on the planet that I can't beat in a fight" Lonnegan is as mad as a box of frogs. He's about thirty-five. He once glassed a bloke in the face for standing on his toe in a nightclub. About eight months later he saw him in the Asda, and glassed him again. With a bottle of salad cream. He's spent nearly half his life in the shovel.

Terry Lonnegan is about thirty. He's the "quiet one". Apparently he's got a protection racket going. In France. He goes to France once a month on the ferry and gets protection money from some shopkeepers and bar owners. Apparently.

Gaz Lonnegan, short for Gareth, not Gary. That's what he always says to people who call him Gary. He's about twenty-eight and he's got a burnt face. Looks scary, man. They say it was his father who burnt him, poured a boiling pan of gravy over his face when he was about fifteen. Don't know what for. And I'm not gonna ask him either. He's just got out of the shovel this week. That's the reason they're all out, celebrating. He was doing two years for GBH, but he ended up doing nearly four. The reason he got the extra time was this... His girlfriend had gone to visit him and he was giving her a hard time, accusing her of having affairs and all that kind of shite that nutters do when they're in jail. He was getting madder and madder with her, when he jumped up, put his great big hands around her head, his big sausage thumbs across her eyes, and pushed her eyes in. Pushed her eyes right inside her head. I think she finished with him after that.

Baz Lonnegan, now he is a strange creature. All the rest of the Lonnegans are white with brown hair. Their parents are both white. But Baz isn't, he's black. Not proper black, he's kinda mixed race looking; looks a bit like Will Smith but with ginger hair. A big ginger afro. Mad. The others always tell him he's a throwback, that they must have had black relatives or ancestors or something. But the rumour goes that Old Ma' Lonnegan was having it away with some Jamaican bus driver during the '70s. It's only a rumour though. I don't know if he had ginger hair. And I'm definitely not asking them that.

Last, but certainly by no means least, there's Finbar. Freaky Finbar. He's the youngest. About twenty-one, I think. But being the youngest makes him think that he's got something to prove, that he's got to be madder than the rest of them. That he's got to be madder than *anyone*. He will stab you as soon as look at you. It seems like he was born to hate. He is always paranoid, always thinks that everyone's talking about him, when they're not – they're probably talking about Baz and his crazy ginger afro. He has committed so many acts of mindless violence that I don't even know where to begin. I'll just give you a little idea of what he's like, if you haven't already started to imagine. He was in a pub in town once, Fat Sally's, with a few of his friends. I was DJing in there at the time, up on the stage where I could see everything that went on. Anyway, the place was packed to the rafters, everyone was getting rat-arsed, and Finbar and his troop were being extremely noisy and obnoxious, banging in to people on purpose and shit like that.

'Who the *fuck* are you lookin at?' Finbar had just chosen some little guy at random to direct his hate at. The poor bloke had only glanced at him whilst looking around the bar. He didn't answer Finbar, just looked away and carried on with his drink. Freaky Finbar flew over to him, grabbed him by the throat and screamed in his face, 'I *said*, who the *fuck* do you think you're fucking looking at? You *cunt*.'

The little guy was petrified. All his friends were petrified too as Finbar's troop gathered around.

'N-n-nobody, m-m-mate. I'm not looking at nobody.'

'So you're calling me a nobody, are you? Well fuck you, cunt. Nobody calls me a nobody and gets away with it. Nobody.'

At this he jerked his head forward and clasped his teeth around the poor guy's chin and bit it off, then his nose. He would have had his ear off too if the bouncers hadn't got over and slung him out. There was claret everywhere, man. The moral of that story has surely got to be that if you are ever in the company of Finbar Lonnegan, don't speak to him and don't look at him. But then he might accuse you of ignoring him, and go mental. You never know.

As it happens, we haven't got a beef with them, they're okay with us, we get on alright with them, it's all hunky dory. But we're still wary of them all the same.

You just know that something bad *will* happen when they are there. They walk in to a place, and ten minutes later the place is nearly empty. Everyone fucks off. Somewhere safe. Well, that's what *normally* happens.

Today, everyone except me and Steve seems oblivious to the Lonnegans. All six of 'em.

We try not to catch their attention. Our plan is to get a drink or two then fuck off.

They don't seem as though they're in a bad mood, as it happens; they're laughing and dancing about. They might be alright today after all. We'll still stay inside though. Just in case.

So that's exactly what we did. The crack was good, we drunk a few brandies, sung Irish songs with the pikeys, even though the music on the jukebox was reggae, ate some drugs and laughed like monkeys, and then… the heavens opened.

Bleedin' bouncing it down. Fucked up, mess your lovely hair up, kinda rain.

Everyone who had been in the beer garden, dancing in the sun, all ran inside for cover.

Including the Lonnegans. All six of 'em.

It got full in the bar very quickly, everyone piss wet through, shaking their hair and the like.

There was this one black guy, sitting all by himself, about my age he was, minding his own business, bobbing his head to the music, drinking his bottle of beer and reading a Sunday paper. I remember looking at him and thinking that I knew him from somewhere. He had a hairlip. It really stood out too. Looked pretty freaky it did. I'd only ever seen one black guy with a hairlip in my whole life. Fuck! It was him. King. Or was it Kong? Doesn't matter, it was one of the cunts anyway.

I told Steve what had happened to me all those years ago at Tiffany's, the full story. He was pissing himself laughing. He thought it was great fun. Then I told him that one of the cunts who made me smear shit all up my own back was sitting in the corner. He stopped laughing.

He walked over to the hairlip guy, snatched his paper from him, rolled it up tight and cracked him around the face with it. Then came the famous Steve line:

'Oy. Cunt. Are you havin' a nice time?'

Before Steve could even finish his sentence, Hair Lip upturned the table toward him, beer and ashtray crap everywhere, and he leapt up at Steve. There was a brief scuffle. The place was packed solid now, everyone soaked through with beer and rain. I flew over to Steve's aid. But just as I got there, Hair Lip pulled out what I thought was a knife and lunged at Steve, screaming 'Bumbo Clart!' or some other form of gibberish. Steve moved to one side and the "knife" went right into Frankie Lonnegan's cheekbone. Blood? It fuckin' pissed out, man.

That was it.

Steve didn't have to say or do another damn thing. Nor did I.

But the Lonnegans did. All six of 'em.

They all waded into poor King, or was it Kong, old Hair Lip.

There was chaos. Everyone moved, made way for the ferocious onslaught that was the Lonnegans.

He'd stabbed Frankie in the face. He had to pay. And pay he did.

They stamped and stamped and stamped on his head. The sounds were sickening, crunching sounds. They booted and booted and hit him with chairs and tables, cast-iron tables. They smashed bottles and ashtrays over his head. Relentlessly they did this, with not a soul going to Hair Lip's rescue. He was unconscious almost instantly, but still they punished him. Finbar, Freaky Finbar, was foaming at the mouth and screaming, 'Die, cunt!' It was like he was having some kind of an epileptic fit or summat, man.

Hair Lip's limp, lifeless body was being jumped on over and over. That black blood was pouring from his ears, brain blood. They each took a penalty kick at his head, one after the other. I swear I thought his head was gonna come off with the force of the boots. Then, after what seemed an eternity, they stopped. Finbar turned and sneered at the crowd. Nobody looked at him though, everyone turning away and not catching his gaze. Just in case. In a final act of menace and pure evil, Freaky Finbar pulled out his knob and started to piss on what looked like a dead Hair Lip, laughing like a nutter shouting, 'The Piss of Death!' Even the other Lonnegans found this a sight too crazy to bear, so Frankie grabbed Finbar and pulled him by the arm as he was still pissing.

They didn't hang about this time though. They didn't wait for the police so they could fight them. No. They were off. They knew they had done some damage. Big jail time damage.

They liked jail. But they didn't want to be there forever. So they fucked off.

FISH, CHIPS AND POTATO PEELERS

All six of 'em.

The chaos continued in the bar, all kinds of other little fights starting, women fighting and pikeys fighting and whoever else fancied their self. So we fucked off too.

On the way out, Steve picked up the "knife" that Hair Lip had lunged at him with. It was on the floor, with Frankie Lonnegan's blood on it. It wasn't a knife. It was a potato peeler. You know the type? With the V-shaped blade?

To think, Frankie Lonnegan is walking around in Hull, or wherever he's from, with a V-shaped scar in his cheek.

Could have been a V-shaped scar in Steve's heart if he hadn't have moved.

But then again, if I'd have kept quiet about Tiffany's and getting shit up my back when I was a young 'un, nothing would have happened at all. I felt a little bit sorry for Hair Lip.

Oh well.

What goes around comes around.

Driving home I was fairly quiet. It had shocked me seeing such a savage, merciless beating.

It made me thank God that it wasn't me. Good job I went to Mass this morning.

Steve was quiet too, staring blankly at the road ahead.

I was concerned for him when he was quiet.

'What you thinking about, Stevie boy?'

He whispered…

'I like stone cladding. It's nice. I might get some.'

CHAPTER FIVE

—

BALD

IT'S THE SECOND MOUSE THAT GETS THE CHEESE
Proverb of unknown origin –
thought to be mid 18th century

AUGUST 1983– AGED 16

Having an intelligent conversation wasn't really one of the things that we aspired to at sixteen years of age. In fact, the more bollocks that was uttered, the better. The bollocks that we spoke was usually in the confines of my bedroom. The *only* place to be, if we weren't at the local disco, or at Tiffany's, or trying unsuccessfully to get into pubs.

My bedroom, you see, had it all. A big sofa, fake leather, on which we could lounge about, two beds on which we could lounge about, a great big brown velvet beanbag, on which we could lounge about, and a huge furry looking rug, on which we could… well, lounge about.

There was a desk in the corner where I used to do my homework. No more homework now though. On the desk was my pride and joy. The stereo. A ghetto blaster to be precise. It played tapes *and* it had a radio, which meant that I, like everyone else in the country, could tape the top forty charts on a Sunday instead of buying the singles in town. This was a method which I had to perfect, as you would frequently get the voice of some inane DJ twittering over the final verse of your favourite tune. Also on the desk was a small portable television, which I only watched on a Thursday at seven, as did all the country, because that's when *Top of the Pops* was on. It was Thursday today. Ace. So there we had it – the comfy surroundings, in which to lounge about, and the music, there always had to be music. My walls were littered with the usual teenage boy kind of crap, posters of Debbie Harry from Blondie and such, but I also had a penchant for the weird and outlandish too. There would be slightly devil worshippy kind of things looking down at me. Pictures of skulls and witches. An actual sheep skull was on the desk. A black candle always burning beside it.

I always had joss sticks burning as well. They only cost a few pence and they'd disguise the smell of the cigarettes that we would smoke. Normal ones or otherwise.

The best thing about my room being the meeting place was that my parents were cush.

They let me take all and sundry up there, no questions asked. Once up there they would rarely interfere with us. My mates' parents hardly let you into the house, let alone the bedrooms.

We loved it. It was our own mini club.

We would pool our money together to buy cigarettes and alcohol. The cigarettes, ten, or if we had a little more cash, twenty, would go into a small vase on the desk, for us to share, pulling them out whenever we wanted. To make the cigs appear to go further we would often share one between three or four of us. This could prove to be quite a trial in itself. Everyone would always want the first part of the cigarette, followed by shouts of 'two's up' for the second part, 'three's up' for the third and so on. However, if you weren't first in line you would be smoking a wet-ended, awful tasting excuse for a cig. It was always soaking wet on the tip. It made you feel sick. A Jew's arse we called it. I have absolutely no idea why. But we still said it. 'Don't *strain* the fucker' was another of the cries you would usually hear as each person sucked it as though they were trying to pull a football through a straw. There have been occasions when I've seen twelve people share one cigarette. It fucks it up, man. Nasty. Then the last person to have a go, the smallest guy usually, would have to smoke the filter. You would hear almost tearful cries of 'I'm not smokin' the brown bit.' I had to smoke the brown bit once, the filter; it's filled with cotton wool so doesn't make for a very satisfying smoke, I can tell you. All this black shit went in my mouth. Like I said, nasty.

The alcohol was more important than the cigs to us. We were allowed to smoke, so that was no big deal. But we weren't allowed to drink yet. So that made it more fun.

Buying it sometimes proved to be tricky, but we always found a way. Nature always finds a way. We would scour the area looking for shops that didn't know how old we were, in the hope of buying some ourselves. If that failed we would just wait outside for a man to walk in and we'd ask him to assist us in our plight. 'Get us some cider, mister. We'll give you a cig.' This method worked quite well until one day we gave our money to some fucker who just took it and then told us to get fucked and ran off. Bastard.

Most of the time we'd get one of our older mates to buy it for us. It was easier. It might cost us a can of ale but it didn't matter, it was worth it.

Cider was the main drink. Cheap and nasty and got you pissed quickly. If we were flush though we might pool together to buy some whisky or Pernod as well. Today we were flush, Mel had just got some birthday money, so today we had twenty cigs, four litres of cider *and* a litre of Pernod. We had to celebrate Mel's birthday in style, didn't we?

We'd already decided not to even try to get into a pub tonight; getting knocked back is such a showing up. No, we'll all stay at mine and party in my room. Party Hearty Marty.

There were four of us that night: my good gorgeous self, his Melness, whose sixteenth birthday we were celebrating, Ricko and Young Mark. We'd invited some girls to join us but they were coming later, at seven-ish, in time for *Top of the Pops*. It was only quarter past five now.

We'd started to discuss the virtues of alcohol and the ways in which we get could absolutely steam faced drunk before the girls arrived.

'Just guzzle as much down as you can, as fast as you can, man,' was my bright idea.

'Fuck that, Gaz...' Mel shook his head furiously, 'that'll just make us all sick, not stink faced. What we gotta do is just drink normally but flick us ash off us cigs intut cider; ash makes you pissed quicker.'

Young Mark nearly freaks out. 'I'm not drinkin' ash! That *will* make me sick.'

'He's right, Mel...' Ricko pipes in, 'all that "ash makes you steamin'" shite is just that – shite, man. I say we go wi' Gaz's idea and just drink as much as we can, right fast an' that.'

Mel's not convinced.

'Look, you lot do what you want, but it's *my* birthday and I'm putting ash in me beer, okay? I wanna be well nutted when the lasses get 'ere, boys.'

Cries of 'sound' and 'sorted' and 'cush' and 'cheers' echo around the room, Mr David Bowie on the radio belting out his latest hit, *Let's Dance*. Awesome song. We loved David Bowie.

So there we were, throwing cider down our gullets, smoking our heads off, laughing and joking, talking gibberish, but mostly taking the piss out of Young Mark.

'When were't last time you 'ad a shag, Mark?' Mel knew that Mark had *never* had a shag when he asked this, y'know, just to embarrass him into telling us some sort of lie that we could all laugh at.

'Erm… let me think…' Mark tapped his chin as if trying to remember. This action caused uproarious laughter from the rest of us. 'Why are y'all laughing? I have *had* a shag, y'know.'

'Yeh? When…?' I laughed at his "I'll convince them" sort of tone. 'And what's more, who with? Who did you shag? Eh? Eh? Come on, man, spill the beans.'

Still tapping his chin, 'Erm… I know, on holiday, yeah, that's when?' He didn't sound very convincing.

Ricko's turn for a bit of mockery. 'Fuck off on holiday. When?'

'When I went to Brid. I stayed in a caravan wi' me nana and shagged a bird then. She were called… Erm… Claire. Yeh, Claire, that's it. Lovely she were. It were ace, man. It were right lovely. She said she loved me.'

My turn, still laughing, 'Go bollocks, man, everyone who's *never* had a shag *always* says they 'ad one on 'oliday. That way no-one can prove you wrong. Or no-one can go straight up to the bird and ask her, and then embarrass the fuck out of you when she says "Did he fuck shag me". You know you're lying, Mark, just admit it, man. Don't be ashamed of yourself for not being able to get a bird. *Ever.*'

Mark's face is bright red and he shouts back at me, 'Fuck you, Gaz man. Anyway, you've only had *one* shag. And she were fucking *bald*!'

Everyone creased up laughing at this announcement. Including me.

'She weren't bald when I shagged her, you mad ginger cunt...' They're all proper pissing themselves now. 'She were nice when I shagged her, man. She just went mad or summat afterwards and went and shaved her head bald. She looked a right bastard after that. So I chucked her. For being bald. Me dad went mad wi' me. He told me you can't treat girls like that, chuckin' 'em just coz they got their head shaved bald. Fuck him, man. I'm not going out wi' no *baldie*. Shame though coz she looked fit before that. Oh well.'

Mark looks pissed off that I didn't get mad at his bald statement, just took it in my stride. I felt a little sorry for him then, so I changed the subject.

'Anybody pissed yet? I am a bit. C'mon, let's open that Pernod, boys.'

Now, Pernod, for any of you unfamiliar with the drink, is an aniseed-based spirit. Mental stuff indeed, strong as a bastard. You need to mix it with lemonade or blackcurrant juice, however, coz if you drink it neat you will be comatose. We had neither. All we had to mix it with was cheap cider. Strong, cheap cider. Oh well, here goes nothing.

'Here's what we'll do, boys...' I pretend that I'm the big drinking authority, 'we'll bang some Pernod in our glass, top it up wi' cider and then slam it on the desk and down it in one, just like cowboys do off the telly, yeh?'

'What's the idea behind that, then?' Ricko looks puzzled as he asks.

Mel thinks he knows the answer. 'I think it's when you slam it on desks and that, the sugar all turns into a hundred and fifty proof alcohol or summat. And fucks yer brains out. Is that right, Gaz?'

'I don't know what it does, man, but I do know that it gets you mental, so come on slam away, boys, the girls'll be here in twenty minutes.'

So we did. Each of us poured what would probably be a quadruple measure in a pub of Pernod into a half-pint glass, topped it up with paint-stripper strength cider, then *BANG*. Slam on the desk, up to the gob and down in one. Like a cowboy.

'*Fuuuuuking bastard nasty fuckin'yaaak!*' coughed Mel.

My reaction wasn't much better, '*Aaaaaaaaaaaaaaaarrgh!*'

Ricko fell to his knees clutching his throat as though he was gonna die. '*Fack, fack, fack, me neck's on bastard fire. Faaaaaaaaak!*'

And poor Mark, only fourteen and all, well he screamed like a woman, really high-pitched screaming like you hear on horror movies when women are being chased by mad killers.

'Gaz, what de *FEK* is going on up dere?'

Oh no, it was my dad shouting from the bottom of the stairs. He sounded quite mad coz he said fek, which he says "is not swearin', it's an Irish terminology" but it still lets me know that he's angry.

I shout back down through the gap in the door, trying to compose myself after the terror that was Pernod and Fire in my oesophagus, 'Nowt, Dad, Mark... erm... er... cut himself...He cut himself shaving.'

I realise what I've just said and bite my lip, the others in the room laughing under their breaths so that my dad can't hear them.

'Ah well,' shouts my dad, 'probably serves him right, lettin' you little feks teach him how to shave. Behave yourselves now.'

I hear the living room door slam. He's gone back in to my mam. No questions asked. He actually thought Mark'd cut himself shaving. Is my dad pissed as well?

I pop my head back in the bedroom, my head that's spinning like a record, and the guys are all laughing at what my dad said. They couldn't believe it either. Mad.

Now we're all really giddy. The Brain Juice has gone straight to our heads, just as we wanted it to.

'Gaz…' It was me dad again.

Oh no, was he gonna come upstairs and see us all paralytic and stove all of our heads in coz he's six foot one and built like a brick shithouse and we're not?

'Gaz, Bananarama are here. I'll send 'em up, okay?'

Thank fuck for that. He's not coming up to kick ten barrels of shite out of us, it's just the girls, the girls have arrived. Yes. Bananarama my dad calls them; they look a little like the '80s girl group of the same name, hair all backcombed, *big* hair, little crop tops in fluorescent colours, and the tiniest little rara skirts that you could ever imagine – sexy as fuck, man. There's three of them too, just like Bananarama. Come to think of it, *our* girls were fitter than the group.

There was Anita. She was the one that Mel fancied. She fancied him too so he was gonna be cush. She had a little party piece that she would do for us when she got drunk. She could fanny fart at will.

Yep, fanny fart. She would just hitch up her skirt and *PPPPPRRRRRRRRRRRRRPHHT*! It was sure to brighten up even the most miserable of days. It would have you in stitches, man. A very pretty, sweet looking, angelic face, petite and everything, and the maddest noise erupting from her fanny. Hilarious. Especially when you're only sixteen.

There was Jo-Jo. She was *FIT*, man. We called her "the little bit of fitness" on account that she was only little, about four foot eight, and she was super fit. Jo-Jo was mine. Not yet, but it was on the cards. I could tell by how she looked at me, she was gonna be mine. Soon.

Last but by no means least there was Trisha. She was quieter than the other two, who were very brash to put it mildly, but Trisha was more ladylike. She conducted herself well in public, she didn't drink a lot, didn't smoke, wouldn't even kiss a lad, let alone shag one. Aw that's sweet. None of us fancied her. She was very beautiful, but that was no good if she was saving herself until she was thirty fucking five. But she always tagged along with the others.

We didn't mind. It made us look good having three gorgeous birds with us all the time. Ricko once hinted that he might give Trisha a go, y'know try and get off with her, but we put him off by saying that her fanny was probably scabby and that's why she didn't let anyone near it.

When they walked into my room we were all laughing and giggling like schoolgirls. We were well gone now. We did, however, try our best to look and act sober for the girls.

Didn't work.

'Wahey, the *shag pieces* are here!' *Aw fuck! What have I said?* 'I mean… sorry, ladies… the *girls* are here… our *beautiful* girls.'

I know I've gone red-faced. I can't believe I called them shag pieces to their faces. Fuck.

'You better behave yourself, little fella, or we'll just turn back around and go find some boys who'll treat us like ladies.' Jo-Jo said this with a wry smile on her face, as though she may have secretly thought that being called a shag piece was funny.

'C'mon, sit yer sens down, *ladies*.' Mel gave me a swift disapproving glance and mouthed the words, 'Shut the fuck up' at me. He was worried I was going to spoil his chances of a shag. 'Gaz was only messin'. 'ere, 'ave a drinky wink.' He passed them all a glass each of our flames-in-a-glass concoction.

Anita looked at hers curiously. 'You're not trying to get me drunk are you, Mr Mel?'

'Would I?' He winked at us. 'I'm sure you can do *that* all on your own.'

And she could. Anita was renowned for being able to drink the lads under the table at any party. Shlurp. There. It was gone, up to her gob, down the neck. In one go. No screaming, no clutching the windpipe. Nothing. What a girl.

'Pass me another, Mr Mel.' She whispered this in her most overtly flirtatious Marilyn Monroe voice.

Fucking hell, I could see how this was gonna go now as Mel sidled up to Anita on the bed and brushed us all away. He was gonna get his nuts, and we were all gonna have to watch. Fuck *that* for a game of soldiers. I'm not watching no twat get his nuts if I'm not getting mine.

They both climbed up onto the top bunk and started to kiss and grope and slurp in a way that only teenagers know how.

Ricko and Mark, slurring and giggling, both edged either side of Virginal Trisha on the sofa and started talking complete bollocks to her, the weather and shit like that. Bloody weather? I needed a plan. Jo-Jo was kind of laid across the rug on the floor nodding her head back and forth in time to *Bad Boys* by Wham, singing along to the lyrics, she was pretending that I didn't exist. Not good.

I need to get myself down there with her, despite my spinning head and the feeling that I'm gonna spew everywhere. I need to talk about something cute to her. Girls like cute things, don't they?

So here I am, coming in from behind, closing right up against her laid out, and she's not stopping me. Good.

She's smiling. She *wants* me to cuddle up behind her. Awesome.

My mind is in a real muddle; it's full of Pernod and cider. My guts are swirling, swooosh.

C'mon, Gaz, speak, say something cute, she'll love it.

Here goes…'Jo-Jo?'

'Yeah?'

She was gorgeous, man, even the way she said yeah was gorgeous. She definitely was *The Little Bit of Fitness*.

'Jo-Jo, have you er, er…'

I'm trying my damnedest to pluck something cute from my imagination, whilst all the time listening to Mark and Ricko boring Trisha to death on the sofa and the faint moans of Anita and Mel on the top bunk doing whatever the fuck the lucky bastards were doing.

Something cute… something cute… Think, man, think.

'Have you ever… Have you ever been *shagged up yer arse?*'

Aw bastard! *That* is most definitely *not* what I meant to say. No no no no. Not at all cute.

That was it, man. Jo-Jo jumped to her feet, shaking her arms about and calling me a cheeky bastard – did I think she was some kind of slag, you're a fucking bastard, Gaz, and a torrent of other shite-filled obscenities. She was *not* happy. Ricko and Mark were pissing themselves on the sofa. They thought it was oh so hilarious, especially when she gave me a slap around my chops. Trisha, "I'm a virgin forever even when I find Mr Wonderful" Trisha, started giving me a hard time as well – I should know better than to speak to a lady like that and I had no respect and blah blah fucking blah.

Mel and his wife are taking no notice at all, they're too busy slap, slap, slapping away.

Bastards.

Jo-Jo and Trisha have had enough. They grab their bags and they're gone, door slammed behind them and *still* calling me names as they trot off down the stairs.

Now I'm sad. Very sad. I sit down next to Ricko and Mark, who are both laughing their tits off at me while trying to see what Mel's up to with mucky Anita.

I'm just about to tell them both to fuck off out of my house and go and shag in the park or somewhere when…

'That's me done! Who's next?' Mel was popping his head up from underneath the quilt when announcing this…

We couldn't believe it. Did he mean it? Would she be game for a full-on gang bang? Only one way to find out.

All aboard the Anita Train.

Me, Mel, Ricko and Young Mark, yes even "I've had a shag on holiday" Mark. And poor young Anita. She didn't know what had hit her. She couldn't walk for a week.

I never saw Trisha the Virgin ever again after that night. I did hear that she found Mr Wonderful though – some fucker who got her pregnant at seventeen and beat her to a pulp on a daily basis.

Jo-Jo, aaahhhhhhh Jo-Jo, The Little Bit of Fitness, I never saw her again after that either. Someone told me they saw her in the Fish Market a few years later, with a couple of kids in tow, and that she should now be called The Big Bit of *Fatness*. A pity, that.

And as for Anita, I never saw her again either, but she did teach me a valuable lesson that I wouldn't forget.

The lesson was simple…There are only two types of women: those who are available… and those who aren't.

Like I said… simple.

AUGUST 1996 – AGED 29

'Looky, looky, look, look, looooog!! Fuckin''ell, Steve man, you're missing all the action.'

I've got my head hanging completely out of the car window, ogling the half-naked, sun-kissed beauties that the summer sun always brings to the streets, and Unsolved's sitting tap, tap, tapping into his bastard phone. Not staring at birds.

'Shhh, Gaz man.' He didn't even look up to shush me, he'd just pulled the car over onto the park and started pissing about with his mobile. 'Just shhh! I'm trying to confrabulate.'

I chuckle to myself. '*Confrabulate*. Good word, Steve man. I like it. What ya trying to confrabulate about? Even though it doesn't mean *anything at all*.'

'I'm texting Tony the Toe about that thing...' He gives me a side glance as though I'd just wiped shit on his nana's eyelid, '*oh-fuckin'-kay?*'

I turn back away from him and peer out onto the park at the bevy of women sunning themselves on the grass, all the while thinking about "that thing" with Tony the Toe.

Tony the Toe.

Fuck. Where do I start about Tony the Toe?

I know. Why is he called Tony the Toe? Here's why.

Tone used to work in the mill a few years ago, a real good job it was too, well paid. A wood cutter or lathe operator, or something. Anyhoo, whatever he did involved using one of those great big circular saws, the ones that the baddie always had on *Batman* in the '60s and they'd tie Batman and Robin to a desk to get sawed to death. But they always escaped. One of *those* saws.

He worked away from England quite often – France, Belgium, Eastern Europe, all over the place. This one time, they sent him to Lithuania to work for a month.

So he's sawing away, minding his business, as you do. Pushing this fat chunk of maple toward the Bat Saw he was, singing along at the top of his voice to the Lithuanian radio, apparently, when... *splooge*! He not only pushed the maple into the teeth, but his thumb too. Came clean off. They say that it squirted blood out like comedy blood off a cartoon or Monty Python. Tony, God bless his cotton socks, didn't scream and act like a girl, nope, he just stood and watched in awe as his newly removed thumb flew through the air and into the wood pulping machine. It was like throwing a kitten into a kitchen blender and leaving the lid off. Tiny little splodges of thumb exploded everywhere. Guys were covered in blood and bits of bone and whatever else kind of slime comes out of an exploded thumb. Even though the prospect of ever having his thumb sewn back on had just been thrown entirely to the wind, Tony, God bless him, still stood there, not saying a damn word.

Shock, they said.

His workmates and supervisors, however, were in chaos. Rushing around like blue-arsed flies, no time for an ambulance. There's blood still pissing out of Tony's hand where his thumb used to be, so they had to wrap a towel around it and race him to hospital in one of the work vans.

So, he's in the hospital and the doctor tells him, in broken English and bits of Lithuanian, that they can fix it for him, no problem. Even though he's had the thumb ground into prime mince, they could get him one from someone who had only just come into hospital minutes earlier and died in the emergency room. Car crash victim. Tony agreed to this. He didn't relish the thought of having a dead Lithuanian's thumb but it was better than walking around for the rest of his natural with a twat of a claw looking hand.

So down he went for the thumb to get stitched on. The *dead* thumb.

Four hours later Tony comes around in his bed, surrounded by doctors, feeling groggy, and he asks if the operation was a success.

'Well…' The doctor sounded unsure as he tapped a pencil on his forehead. 'Yes… And No.'

Tony was puzzled. He lifted up his hand to find it bandaged, but in his half drugged state began to rip at the bandage. The doctor tried to stop him but it was too late – the bandage was off and Tony let out an eardrum-penetrating wail of horror. What he saw before him was the stuff of nightmares, Edgar Allan Poe style. There, attached to his hand, where he thought he was going to see a lovely new thumb, albeit a dead Lithuanian thumb, was a toe. A big, *fuckoff toe.*

A swollen dead toe, all purple and nasty, with a gnarly yellow nail on it, the kind of nail that you would only find on a big, dead toe.

He went berserk. They say it took nine doctors to subdue him that day; he's a big lad is Tony.

Apparently, the reason for the big toe was that after the promise to make his hand look better, the doctors put Tony to sleep and took him into theatre only to realise that there had been a mix-up somewhere along the line of communication. This dead guy had lost both his hands in the fire that had ensued when his car crashed, and the doctors thought they were giving his toes to some poor sod who'd lost a toe at work. They didn't want Tony to wake up with nothing. So on went the toe.

He's grown used to it over the years, but it's never blended in properly. It's still purple and it's still too massive for his hand, although the gnarly nail has come off and never grown back.

It looks a bastard really. But no-one tells Tony. Because he's *insane.*

And no-one calls him Tony the Toe to his face, that's for sure.

And… he hates Lithuanians.

'Looooooooooooook, Steve man, there's fanny everywhere.'

I'm still giddy as hell, but Steve, well, he just throws his phone onto the back seat, revs up the engine, cranks up the music and, with an angry sneer in his coke-fuelled voice, gives me a side look and…

'C'mon… we're off to meet that fuckin' freaky, big, ugly, toe-fingered bastard.'

Oh fuck. I've heard that tone before.

'Yer don't like Tony the Toe, do yer, Steve man?'

'No!' A short and sweet answer if ever I heard one.

'Aw c'mon, Stevie, he's alright, man. What's he ever done to you?'

'He's a fuckin *'slink*. That's what he's done to me...' He's getting mad with himself now.

'A *FUCKIN'* slinky, two-faced, grassing, robbing, sly, sell his own granny, burgle my house and deny it, fucking slink. That's all.'

I smile at him. 'Oh, that's okay, then. You shoulda said.'

He smiles back at me and laughs a little.

We have to drive about three miles to meet Tony, at some posh pub in North Leeds. All the pubs are posh in North Leeds. All the people who frequent said pubs think that they're posh. Some of 'em are posh. But a high proportion of them are just criminals, living it up in their million-pound houses and grassing the small fry to the police whenever they can.

A top of the range Mercedes glides past us as we enter the "Posh Zone".

Steve is mesmerised by it. He rotates his head a hundred and eighty degrees to admire it.

'Gaz man... now *that* is *class*. Did you see that motor? Fuckin' class.'

Cars have never bothered me that much. I like a nice motor but I'd never spill me milk over one.

'Yeah it's nice enough, Steve man... but did you see the state of the wanker driving it? A little baldie fucker. Wi' glasses on.'

Steve laughs. 'Yeah man, he's probably got a little dick too. Drives that fancy car to compensate.'

'Naw, Stevie boy, I have to disagree. I have this theory about dicks, ya see.'

'Go on, Gaz man, what's your theory about dicks, then? You've got a theory about fuckin' *everything*, man.'

I proceed with my theory, taking little delicate puffs of my cigarette as I go.

'My theory is *this*. There is no such thing as a small dick or a big dick. Everyone has more or less the same size dick. Course, there are the odd exceptions, like Big John Holmes and his fourteen-inch monstrosity or that bloke in the magazine that we saw with the one-inch dick. But they *are* exceptions. Apart from those kinda guys, everyone has the same size dick. More or less. However, if you take someone such as me – I'm only five foot seven and nearly ten stone, not exactly a big motherfucker by any stretch of the imagination. Am I?'

Steve's chuckling at me. 'No, Gaz man. In fact you could be construed as a little cunt.'

'Exactly, Stevie baby. That's *exactly* what I am. A little cunt. But then, if you take someone like Big Andy McBeth, the bulging bastard. Six foot ten steroid-busting fucker that he is. Stand the two of us next to each other. Naked. Then it is I who will look as though I'm hung like a donkey, innit? I'm not of course, mine's only nine inch, but my theory is that because he's so big, his dick, that's the same size as mine, will look teeny weeny in comparison to the rest of his body building, fuck off, muscly body. Won't it? Same dick size, different body size. No small dicks. No big dicks. Just same dicks. For everyone. There you go, that's my theory.'

'It's a good theory, Gaz man. I like it.' Steve laughs again. 'So, what you're sayin' is that me an' you have got the same size dick as Big Andy McBeth?'

'Yep. Same size, but ours look bigger coz our bodies are smaller. And, Stevie boy, if you want to create the effect of a couple more extra inches, all you gotta do is shave your pubes bald, man. Adds two full extra inches if you get ridda the bush. Bald as a bastard. Like that cunt's head that were drivin' that Merc.'

'Now *that's* a good idea, Gaz man. Does it work?'

In the most nonchalant tone I can muster, 'Course it works, man, I've been doing it for years. Two extra inches. Hung like a fuckin' horse me. Or at least it *looks* like I am.'

Steve's amazed at my bald method. 'Sheesh, as soon as we've done this thing I'm off straight home to shave me knob, Gaz man. Mine's like a bastard jungle. Y'can hardly see me knob for pubes. Fuckin' good idea. Shave the fuckers off. Cheers, mate, yer a pal. I always thought I had a small knob, but it were just me knacker hairs, man.'

We pull up to the pub where Tony the Toe is waiting with his friends. They are all sitting in the beer garden soaking up the sun. As we pull around the car park, I look out across the beer garden and, *Fuck. No.*

Barry, the fucker I sold the dodgy glucose to last year, is sitting in Tony the Toe's crowd.

And he's got some *mean* looking fuckers with him.

Fuck.

'Steve man, fuck this. I can't go in there. I'll get lynched. I ripped that fucker off and I know it'll get fuckin' nasty. There's only two of us. Fuck it, I'm not off in there. We'll get *killed*.'

Steve remains as calm as ever. He just pulls over the car and looks up to the beer garden and says to me, smiling, 'Chill, Gaz man. Fuck 'em in the eye. They're only cunts.'

I'm sweating like the horse I'm hung like. 'Cunts? Cunts? *I know that*, ya mad bastard. *That's* why I don't wanna go in. They're only cunts. What a comment.'

Stevie boy winks at me and then digs deep into the inside pocket of his leather jacket, pulls out the sharpest looking knife I've ever seen in my life and plonks it on the dashboard. Inside his other pocket, another knife, a little smaller, a flick-knife. Jeans pocket next – he pulls out a three-inch canister of CS gas and a gramme of coke. He flicks the switchblade and sticks it into the coke bag, shovels half of it out and up his nostril.

'*Aaaaaargh*! Now *that* hit the fuckin' spot, Gaz man. By the way, y'know that big cunt we were just on about? Andy McBeth? Well, I've heard that some crazy little fuckers went into his bedroom last week and poured petrol on him while he were asleep and set light to him. Burned him up good style. Just thought I'd let y'know. He knacked you years ago, dinny? Serves him right then, dunnit? The fat cunt. Wait here, I'll be back in a quick.'

He's wired for sound now is Stevie boy, grabs his "utensils", jumps out of the car and straight over to Tony the Toe, while I'm sliding down my seat to escape from sight. It's gonna go pear-shaped. I know it is. This is bad.

He marches up like a man on a mission.

There are about twenty-five people in the beer garden and about eight of those are with Tony and Barry.

Most of the people don't even see Steve. They're too busy eyeing up the two young blonde girls who have turned up in their bikinis.

Tony the Toe raises his hand and slowly waves it in front of Steve, obviously trying to get him to see the gnarly disfigured toe thumb.

'Nice to see you, Steve, you wanna drink?' He wiggles his wrist when talking and this gives the effect that the toe is moving of its own accord.

Steve's on Planet Pluto, up there with the fuckin clouds. 'No, I don't want a drink. Just give me the stuff and let me get fucked off.'

'Whoa, boy, calm down, Steve. What's the rush? Meet my friends.' He points to Barry and the meatheads and starts to introduce them, when…

'I said…' Steve's slavering now, like a deranged mental patient, 'give me the stuff and let me get fucked off. I don't care two *fucks* about your cunt mates. How's *that* grab ya?'

Fuck. Not again.

The meatheads who were sitting with Barry took exception to this and jumped up from the bench as if to punch Steve but…

Stab!

Bald meathead number one gets the sharpest knife ever seen straight through his kidney.

Spray!

He gasses every fucker else. CS gas in all of their faces.

Now, I'd never seen the joys of CS gas until that day, and let me tell you it is the business. Those boys all went down like sacks of shite. Clutching their throats and screaming like babies. Rubbing their eyes like they were kneading bread. Everyone in the beer garden was affected, all rolling around on the ground. The passing traffic must have thought it was some kind of posh game. Steve leaned down to Tony the Toe, who couldn't see a thing, eyes all swollen with the gas, put his hand inside Tony's coat and pulled out a parcel and sneered.

'Cheers, Tone. I'll take this, shall I? See ya later, ladies. Hope you had a nice time.'

At this he marched back over to the car, Barry, Tony the Toe and all the meatheads screaming and writhing away behind him.

He calmly opened the car door, threw what appeared to be a fuck off bag of coke onto the back seat and said, 'Never, *ever*, underestimate the power of weaponry. Ha ha ha. Look at them fuckers now, Gaz. Look at 'em. I told you I didn't like that fuckin' slink. Well, now look at him. Ha ha ha ha ha. You see, Gaz man, I've got *my* theory too. Me an' you are only small fellas. We can't fight really, not if we're up against some big bastard. We just can't win. Fact. So it then follows that if we can't win we must resort to drastic action, be madder than the big cunts. You see, Gaz man, it's not the size of the dog in the fight, but the size of the fight in the dog. If you or me don't resort to using a weapon, then we'll get killed to death, man. If a big cunt is gonna start on a little cunt like me or you, then he's a fuckin' bully, an' bullies deserve to lose. Just like that cunt Andy Mc*Fuckin'* Beth who got burned up last week. What I just did to them cunts was self-defence anyway. Don't let it worry ya.'

I was amazed at his theory and how he thought he was in the right because they were bigger than us...

'That, Stevie boy, was *not* self-defence. They didn't do fuck all to you. You just went apeshit and started stabbin' cunts and spraying fuckers so you could steal their drugs. Self-defence? Fuck no, man.'

He was meaner looking than ever now, stared straight at me, not caring that the fuckers were all still rolling around in agony just yards away, not even attempting to drive away before the cops come.

'Gaz... baby... it was *pre* self-defence. It's the law, man. The law states that if you feel that you're being threatened you can use reasonable force to defend yourself, even if they haven't already attacked you. It's the law.'

I'm intrigued. 'So, you stabbing a cunt in the kidney and spraying CS gas in everyone's faces and nearly blindin' and chokin' every fucker is what you would consider *reasonable* force?'

'Yep. It's like this, Gaz – the law says that if you *think* you are gonna be killed by a weapon, then you have the right to use the same weapon on them. Retaliate first! It's true. If I got caught for this and got sent to court, I'd just tell the judge that I thought they all had guns. I'd get away with it too; they've all been in trouble for firearms in the past. I'd get clean away with it, man. There's not a judge in the land who'd lock you up for stabbin' an' sprayin' them cunts. Unless you were black. N*****s don't get away with fuck all.'

A bit of unnecessary racism there, but he's right I suppose.

A siren could be faintly heard in the distance. That was Steve's cue. He calmly switched on the engine, revved up the motor and screeched off. I just smiled nervously and nodded to the music. To tell you the truth, he was scaring me. Was he going mad or summat? It seemed that every time I met him something stupid would happen. It had to stop.

'What you thinkin' about, Gaz man?'

I didn't dare tell him that I was thinking about him being a mad bastard. He was still sweating and evil looking and might take it the wrong way.

'I'm thinking about you gettin' home and shaving your knackers down to the wood. That's what.'

He stopped the car with a screech. Stared me straight in the eye and…

'*That* is a fuckin' good idea, Gaz man. Two more inches. *Yes. Yes. YES!*'

Then he leaned over and gave me great big, smacking kiss on the lips.

CHAPTER SIX

—

HUBBLE BUBBLE

PAIN DON'T HURT

Dalton (Patrick Swayze)–
RoadHouse– 1989

MARCH 1984 — AGED 16

I'd love to be able to say that my upbringing was terrible, that my parents were alcoholic wastrels who gambled the rent money away and injected drugs. I'd love to be able to say that I was beaten daily and neglected and left to fend for myself from the age of five. I'd love to say that my mother was on the game and my father had a string of dog-ugly mistresses.

But I can't. Those kinds of stories make you wanna slash up, man.

My parents were fantastic. Simple as that.

Their love for one another was only outweighed by the love they felt for me and my sister and two brothers. We never wanted for anything. We never had lots of money as such, but we were well cared for. My father was a giant of man, a giant Irishman who came over to England in the '60s to find work. He was in the building trade and they were on strike in Ireland. He soon found work in Birmingham and then moved to Leeds in about '65 where he met me mam. They fell in love, got married and had me in '67. My sister followed in '69 and then there was a gap of a few years before my brothers came in '75 and '79. The family was now complete. Great big Catholic family. Cush.

My dad worked like a dog, day in and day out, breaking his back as a plasterer and assorted other donkey work type jobs.

Until now.

Now, ladies and gentlemen, my life was about to change forever.

My parents bought a *pub*.

Here's me, nearly seventeen years of age, living in a *pub*. There is a God.

'What's the name o' this pub yer dad's gettin', Gaz?' Mel sounded really excited at the fact that one of us was gonna have our very own beer shop.

I was excited too. I couldn't wait to move in. Only a week until the details went through and then we'd be there.

'The Fanchester Arms. You might know it as The Fanny. Have y'ever been?'

Mel took a sharp intake of breath as though to scare me. 'Ooooh, Gazzy boy. Not The Fanny. You'll need ya fightin' boots on if you move there, mate. It's a right rough hole. I swear.'

He giggles as he tells me, so I can't make out whether he means it or not.

'I don't care, man. It'll be *my* rough hole. That's what counts. Mine!'

You see, it didn't matter to me if it was a rough hole, coz my dad was the hardest man alive. Fists like breezeblocks and an iron punch to match. Any trouble, he'll sort it for me.

Hulk Dad won't let me get into any bother.

ONE WEEK LATER

'C'mon, quick, man, I'm bleeding to death!' We must have already been doing fifty miles an hour as I bellowed to the taxi driver, pressing a blood-soaked towel against my left eyebrow.

'Leeds General Infirmary. Only one moment away, Mr Gaz…' My Asian taxi driver friend, Mumtaz, then tried his hand at humour. The twat. 'You cry like a girl, Mr Gaz. You only have a mere flesh wound and you cry worse than baby. I get worse wound than that on my *sexual organ* and do not cry. I am *man*. When wounded, I, Mr Gaz, begin to laugh. Ha ha har!'

This guy's a crank, no doubt about that. I try to sound more manly:

'Just get me inside the hospital, man, and get some stitches in me fuckin' eyebrow.'

FORTY-FIVE MINUTES EARLIER

I thought I was the bee's bollocks, man. Here I am, in my own pub. Fuckin' ace, man.

We'd all moved in yesterday, got the furniture in, sorted out the bedrooms, who goes where and what goes there and blah blah blah. My dad spent most of the day with the men from the brewery finalising the arrangements and what have ya, whilst I strutted up and down the bar as though I owned the gaff. I got to know some of the locals as soon as I arrived. They seemed a friendly bunch, hardly a tooth between them but friendly all the same. My dad introduced himself to them all.

'I'm John. Howya? This is moy pub, a nice pub, and I'm a nice man. Until it's time to not be nice. Right?'

Good introduction, Dad. I like it.

I don't know if nice was the word that you'd use though. The Fanny had seen better days to say the least. Nothing a lick of paint wouldn't cure.

Anyhoo, here I am, day one in my new found home, and my dad tells me that tomorrow he has to go to Dublin to see my grandad who's ill. He'll only be gone one night and would I watch the bar with me mam. No problem. I'd spent many a night behind the bar in my part-time job, I could pull a mean pint and I got on well with everyone. Everyone.

Off he went to the airport at about four thirty in the afternoon, telling me to be good, look after me mam and the family and that he'd be back tomorrow. It's all good.

Now, the teatime session in The Fanny consisted mainly of guys who'd been out on the building sites all day and came in for a swift gallon before they went home and a few old codgers who'd spent all day keeping warm with their freezing cold pints. How does that work, then? They'd come in to keep warm and order a freezing cold beer. Baffled me. The other type of customers you'd get in at teatime would be the fuckers who had been out all day, round town or somewhere, on a sesh, or a througher. They were the ones you had to watch out for. They could get a bit lively, carrying on and fighting each other. You'd only get those types in on either a Monday, when they'd called in sick to work– The Monday Club– or on a weekend. Today was Wednesday so there should be no problem, right?

Wrong.

It's about 6pm, and the place has got quite a buzz going for a Wednesday, not usually renowned for being a busy night. It always happens apparently when you get a new landlord. Everyone comes to have a nosy. Oh, and all the people who were barred by the previous landlord come back to try their luck. My dad had already said to me that nobody was barred until he barred them. Everyone was welcome, regardless of what they had done in the past. They were welcome until they upset him. Fair enough.

So here I am, looking after the pub on me own, me mam's gone to the supermarket and me brothers and sister are out playing, when in they walk, three, pissed out of their faces, all-day drinkers. The Monday Club… on a Wednesday. Fuck.

Don't worry, Gaz, just treat them like everyone else, keep smiling, tell a few jokes…

'Hiya, gents, what yavvin?' I couldn't be more jovial if I tried.

As mean and surly as they looked at first, I was pleasantly surprised to find that they were quite affable and cheery. There were two monstrous looking, fat fuckers and a skinny fucker with greasy hair and beady eyes. One of the fat fuckers was about six foot ten. Andy McBeth was his name. He had this mashed-in, flat nose as though he was either a boxer, or some fucker had cracked him across his mush with a frying pan. The other fat cunt had a great mass of curly hair all over his head and chin. Flopper they called him. I never found out the skinny beady-eyed bloke's name.

'I'll have a pint of gravy for me and two pints of soup for the lads, mate.'

Big Andy McBeth pointed to the beers that they wanted on the front of the bar as he said this, which is a good job coz I'd have been fucked if I knew what he meant by *gravy* and bleedin'*soup*! He was smiling though so I knew they meant no harm. They were just a bit pissed.

I gave them their drinks and chatted with them for a while, laughing at their jokes, they laughed at mine, a bit of lively banter. The crack was good. They called me names, jokingly, a little twat and shit like that. No harm done. I called them names back, to the tune of much laughter by one and all. These guys are good fun. I like them.

'Gizza cigarette, Gaz, ya little twat.' McBeth smiled as he shouted across the bar to me.

Pulling a pint for one of the other customers I shouted back that I didn't have any cigs then I looked down to see if the pint was full yet.

'*Don't fucking lie, cunt!*' He shouted this so loud that I dropped the drink I was serving, and it smashed at my feet, covering me in beer and glass. His face had changed from being kinda friendly and funny to as though he wanted to do me in. '*I saw you smoking one earlier, ya little rat cunt. Gimme a fucking cig. NOW!*'

Now I was scared. This big fat gloyt was growling at me. Where's me dad? Where the fuck is Hulk Dad when I need him?

'Andy… mate…' I was shaking like a shitting dog now. I knew it was gonna get ugly. 'It were me last one that you saw me smokin'. Honest, mate.'

At that, he didn't say a word, just picked up his pint and threw it at the mirrors behind the bar, smashing everywhere, the pint and the mirror. I cowered in terror as the shards of glass exploded all around me. Almost on my knees behind the bar I looked up to see this brute of a man going fucking wild, destroying everything he could grab hold of – glasses, beer pumps, stools – he then picked up a great thick, glass ashtray, bounded over the top of the bar and sunk it into my eyebrow. *THUD.* It must have weighed at least two pounds. It hurt like fuck. Although dazed and amazed, petrified I leapt to my feet and ran, ran as fast as I could, blood spewing from the gaping wound in my eyebrow, through the pub, out the door and up the fuckin' road I went. Frankie Goes to Hollywood were urging me to *Relax* and shit from the jukebox as I shot off. I didn't stop running until the pub was out of sight, until I could no longer hear Frankie singing. Big McBeth didn't follow, though. He must have still been in there. *Demolishing* the gaff. Aw fuck. My dad's left me in charge and this fat fucker's smashing the place to bits, *and* me mam and the kids'll be back soon. No other way around it, I had to call the police. I sat in the road and waited what seemed like forever for them to come, all the while rivers of blood flowing from my crust.

When they arrived they took me into the pub with them. He was still destroying the place. It was like a bomb had gone off. It took six coppers to hold him down. He was throwing them around like rag dolls. They eventually took him away screaming and howling. I'd never felt as safe in my entire life as when I saw that police car turn the corner with him in it.

My poor mam got back from the supermarket to the devastation that was her new home, she called me a taxi and off I shot to the hospital, my eye still pissing claret.

Mumtaz was right, it was only a flesh wound. Five stitches and a scar for life. A scar on me fuckin' eyebrow. Bastard. My lovely face, ruined. I'll never get a girl again.

I was gutted that my dad wasn't around to save me that night. I felt helpless. It was at that point that I realised I couldn't rely on Hulk Dad anymore. He wasn't always gonna be around, was he?

Me and me mam decided not to tell him what had happened. We'd clean the pub up and tell him that the stitches on my eye were from falling down the cellar steps. He arrived back from Dublin the next day, full of the joys of spring; me grandad was getting better and there was a whole future ahead of us in The Fanny. He burst into the kitchen upstairs where I was nursing my sore head and shouted at the top of his voice:

'*Did I miss anything, guys?*'

SEPTEMBER 1996 — AGED 29

Throughout the '60s and '70s, Leeds was what could only be described as a rat hole. A decaying, industrial wasteland whose only claim to fame was that the Yorkshire Ripper tested his grisly lustings in the back streets.

And Jimmy Savile lived there.

The late '80s and the whole of the '90s, however, saw the powers that be, the faceless "they", knock down old Leeds in favour of an all-singing, all-dancing "bright new future for everybody".

They couldn't have been more misguided.

Yeah, sure, they knocked down the crumbling Leeds. But what they replaced it with was *Fucking London!*

Shiny office blocks and apartments by the river selling for a million pound apiece. Shops and arcades spivving the smartest of cool apparel throughout the city centre. Clubs and bars where only the "beautiful people" could congregate and sip Mexican beer from the bottle with a tiny slice of lime in the neck. Fuckin' lovely.

Not.

The extreme amount of wealth that was pouring into the city was made only too apparent by the abject poverty of the outskirts. The sprawling housing estates where going out after dark was for the badgers. The homeless fuckers on every other street corner. The smack heads on the ones in between. The shoplifters and burglars and prostitutes and pimps, the blaggers and robbers and smugglers and muggers and killers and joyriders and… Need I go on?

Now, when the kids who have to live in these miserable shitholes, and the adults for that matter, see the untold wealth of the city types and top flight criminals, there are only three ways in which to go.

1. Get a job. 'Fuck that,' they say. Working's for fools and horses. Anyway, where y'gonna get a job when you come from the estates? As soon as you apply for something respectable "they" look at your postcode and tell you to fuck off, "they" don't want "your sort".

2. Take enormous amounts of mind and body altering drugs in order to detach oneself from the world. This, my friends, is always a popular option. A dynamic release from the humdrum reality of your unfeasibly dreary existence. The only problem with this option is that it creates a no-win situation. No money to buy drugs, no job to get money to buy drugs, turn to crime to get money to buy drugs, get a criminal record for turning to crime to buy drugs, never get a job for having a criminal record, turn to drugs for not having a job and turn back to crime to pay for drugs to take your mind off not having a job and living on a crime-ridden estate. Or die of an overdose.

3. Sell drugs. Wahey! We like the sound of this one. Not only can you make some cash and buy shit that you won't need, you can get as high as a bastard kite. For free!

    But don't forget, kiddiewinks, no matter how lovely a day it is, no matter how the wind catches the cloth, every kite has to come down. And when it flies too high and you lose a grip of it, it'll come down with a crash. A crash from which it will never recover.

SATURDAY EVENING, 6:40PM

'Aaaaaaaaaw fuck, where amma?'

I forced one eye open to admire my new surroundings. It was like looking through binoculars, the wrong way round and with margarine smeared over the lenses. After pulling at my eyelids and much slapping of my own cheeks, I eventually came into focus and looked down at my watch. I spotted Steve in the corner of the room snorting the longest, fattest line of coke I had ever seen.

'Stevie baby...' I started to focus now, 'where the fuck are we? Who's gaff is this? It stinks. And it's twenty to *fuckin'* seven, man. At night!'

He howled laughing at me and then, 'Wow! That hit the spot...' He shook his head around as though to make the Charlie go into his brain faster. 'Don't you remember coming 'ere this morning, Gaz man? We got 'ere about half eight, after Casablanca's. It's Clockwork John's flat.'

He leaned over and started to snort some more from his three foot line of coke. I'm fully focused now, I can see everything around me – a great big leather sofa on which I'm curled up, a monstrous looking hi-fi system in the corner, a built-in kind of kitchen in the other corner and empty beer cans and bottles strewn all around the place.

'I don't... I can't remember... Fuck... Half eight this morning? Who's Clockwork John? What sort o' name's that? Does he wear loads o' watches or summat?'

I sit up now and grab an unopened bottle of warm lager from the glass coffee table in front of me. There's some crappy music playing in the background. Sounds like supermarket music or something you'd hear in a lift.

Steve wiped the white powder from around his nostrils, gave me a huge smile and proceeded to tell me the what, why, when, where and who of the situation.

'Gazzy, baby… you don't remember? Not at all? Just stand up a sec. Go on. Stand up.'

I leaned forward and placed my feet on the floor. I was about to stand up when…

'AAAARGH! Fuck me. Me bollocks, man!'

And I fell back down onto the sofa, clutching at my belly. I was in the most excruciating pain. I'd felt a throbbing in me knackers when I was lying down, but the pain I felt when I stood up was unbearable. Steve howled laughing at me.

'Do you remember now, Gaz man?'

I lay there trying to recollect the events of the night before when *Ping!* It started to come back to me. I gave a few of the details to Steve and he told his version of other parts of the story.

What had gone on was this. The previous night I'd gone out without Steve. I was gonna meet him in Casablanca's at about two in the morning. Casablanca's was a seedy all-night dancing place where the dregs of the earth danced and ate drugs until dawn. Anyway, I'd gone out on me own to knock out a few Ziggys and some Billy before I went to meet Steve at Casa's. I ended up getting wasted myself and heading to a club called Asia, a place where I was well known and I could make a bit of dosh. The bouncers always turned a blind eye. The trouble was, when I got there, there was a new set of bouncers on the door. No problem, I'll just be a bit more careful.

So there I am, off me nut, lots of people there who I know and lots of people who wanted gear. I was really sly about the deals, real secret agent stuff, slipping them a couple of pills under the table and when I went to greet them, shaking hands and shit. Real sly.

Not fuckin' sly enough.

There'd been a problem with drugs in Asia for a long while now and the management wanted to put a stop to it, hence the new bouncers. They could sniff a dealer at a thousand paces these fellas.

Before I knew what was going on I was being bundled out of the fire door. Three of 'em picked me up and used me as a battering ram. Opened the fucking door with me head they did.

They got me out the back. Fuck. Not out the back. There is no feeling that sums up the fear you feel when you get taken out the *back* by bouncers. You know it's gonna hurt. They went through me pockets and found my stash. About fifteen wraps of Billy and a bag with about forty pills in it. Now, normally what bouncers do when they find your stash is take it off you. That's a dead cert. They then proceed to go back into the club and sell it themselves. Cunts. They then give you a couple of slaps and tell you to go on your way. Not nice at all. But the alternative is them calling the feds and you ending up doing the big bitch in some shitty hellhole of a prison. Bad option.

So here's me expecting to get a couple of punches and to have me gear stolen from me.

There were six of 'em out there with me at this point and the ugliest of them, he looked like a pig, took my pills and emptied them onto the concrete. He smirked at me, then took his big dirty pig-looking foot and stamped all over me pills. Crushed 'em into powder. I was horrified. He could at least have just stolen them and sold them on to make some of the fuckers in the club a bit happier. That was just fucking mean and cruel. Pill-crushing bastard.

He laughed in my face, and then, 'Hold him, boys,' he grunted to his mates. The pig.

Two of them grabbed my arms and pulled me up to the wall. What happened next was awful. Awful, I tell you. I don't like to use the word awful, but this was just, well, *awful*.

Each and every one of the mad, fat, steroid-abusing, no-neck fuckers took a run up to me from about twenty yards and delivered a sickening drop kick to me bollocks, man. The first guy ran up to take his penalty and I screamed in agony and dropped to the floor, a terrible sick feeling coming into my gutty wutts. Coughing and spluttering, they brought me back to my feet and carried on, all taking a kick each. After six kicks they let me fall to the ground in a heap, rolling and writhing like a salted slug. One of them shouted at me to fuck off and never to come back and they slammed the door behind them, going back inside the club. I managed to shuffle to my feet and hobble to the main street where I could sit on a bench and compose myself. My bollocks had been kicked up inside my stomach. Unsolved Steve usually gets me out of these kinds of scrapes. All on me own again, no Hulk Dad and no Steve. What the fuck was I gonna do? I limped up to the hospital and, after waiting an hour surrounded by junkies and prostitutes who'd taken beatings from crazy punters, I was attended to. They assured me that my knackers would drop back down "in their own good time" and that in the meantime there was nothing else they could do for me other than painkillers. The tops of me legs and me groin would be bruised for a couple of weeks and to fuck off on my merry way.

Charming.

It was now about half three in the morning so I set off to Casablanca's to meet Steve, still completely off me face. When I got there and told him what had happened he thought it was oh so hilarious and told everybody else within shouting distance. 'Gaz's knackers are in his belly, not in his knacker sack.' Lovely. Now they all think I'm a bollockless cunt. I stood over a plumped-up beanbag and ate five more pills.

Then collapsed.

The sad thing is that no-one thought that I was dead or in a coma. They just left me to die, for all they knew. Even Steve. It wasn't until closing time at around 7am that Steve lifted me up and took me to a party that he had been invited to at Clockwork John's flat.

SATURDAY NIGHT, 7:35PM

'So you see, Gaz, *that's* what happened to you. And… and… I looked after you and brought you here to Clockwork John's. So you could 'ave a kip.'

I'm bewildered he thinks that letting me collapse in Casa's is looking after me. Well, he *was* out of it himself, I suppose.

I stood up the best I could and walked around a little, the pain in my Smooth Section still unbearable.

'Me Smooths are killin' me, Steve man, I can't let them cunts get away wi' this.' I needed revenge.

Steve crouched back down to his never-ending line of Charlie, took a huge shnerkel and then announced, 'It's all sorted, my son. We gonna get 'em for ya. Tonight!'

He jumped in the air and did a karate chop against the door. He was goin' mad. Too much coke, do you think?

He was shoved out of the way when the door flew open. A crazy looking brute of a lunatic swaggered into the room swinging a walking cane. He had a black bowler hat on and a pair of white dungarees with a crisp white Ben Sherman shirt underneath. And he had a heavily mascarad false eyelash on one eye.

'Hi di hi di hi hi hi there, my little droogy malchiks. What, pray tell, is occurring?' Oh, I get it now. This must be Clockwork John. He stared straight at me, then at Unsolved, then at his watch. 'We meet in Asia. Ten of the o'clock. Tonight. Must leave, many appy-polly-loggies.'

He winked at me with his false eyelash then turned and left, just as fast as he had come in.

'You know some nice fuckers, you do.'

I shook my head as I directed this at Steve and plonked me self down beside him to help him finish his motorway sized line of Charlie.

Steve was in a real agitated state now, hyped up and full of fuck, happy and crazy at the same time.

'John's a good bloke, Gaz. He's gonna help us sort them fucker bouncers at Asia. The cunts. Look what they did to your spuds. It's not on. It's not fuckin' on, man.'

I pulled up from my line of powder. 'Naw, man, it's not on. Me town halls are bastard ruined. So what's gonna happen, then? Tonight?'

Steve fell back into the deep cushions on the sofa and relayed the plan to me. The plan was this.

He was gonna go meet Clockwork at ten o'clock in some pub in town. John would be there with about twenty of his mad bastard Clockwork Orange loving mates, and they were then gonna come to Asia to meet me and to batter the bouncers to within an inch of their bollock-kicking lives.

'Whoa… Steve man…' I cut him short '…what do you mean *meet* me in Asia? Do you want me go back there on me own? Fuck that, man.'

He grins like a Cheshire Cat. 'You'll be cush, Gaz man. Listen to me, calm down. Yes, you do have to go back on your own. But there won't be any bouncers working till ten o'clock. You go in at nine. It's free entry as well at that time. You'll have no problem. I'll give you a bag o' pills to knock out so you can make up for what you lost last night, then we'll come in at ten and knock the fuck out of everybody. Good style. It'll be like the fuckin' Alamo, man. They're not gettin' away wi' bustin' yer knackers in, man. No way.'

With the Charlie now in me brain, I knew he was right. Go in at nine. No bouncers till ten. Make some money. Watch bouncers get destroyed by Steve and Clockwork John's fool friends. I like it. A lot.

So that's it sorted.

I fly home in a taxi and get cleaned up, make myself look hot to trot, and Steve goes off to wherever he has to go in his crazy world of dodgy deals. He gave me a bag of pills to offload in Asia, and he gave me them for *free*. What a mate.

SATURDAY NIGHT, 9PM

Steve was right. As I approached the club I couldn't see a single bouncer. There were long queues of people at the door but no bouncers, just some woman in a long blonde wig letting 'em all in at about ten at a time. Good. My turn to go in. Straight through and down the stairs. My heart was still beating as if it was gonna jump out of me chest though. You never know, the bouncers might be inside, having a drink before they start. You never know.

Once inside, my fears became unfounded – there wasn't a single bouncer in sight. Not even any meatheads, just beautiful people wanting to have a good time. And to take lots of MDMA.

I'm pretty wasted by now, I'm talking Pelican Fly Wasted. The Charlie from earlier on and the three pills I took an hour ago are all takin' their desired effect. I seem to know everyone in the place, and those I don't know seem to know me. The odd stranger prancing around but no-one that looks like the police. I bump into a crowd of girls that I know and sell them a few pills. They love me now. *Everybody* loves the Pill Man.

My plan is to stay with these lasses until Steve gets here, have me self a laugh and a dance before all hell breaks loose. Then, when they do arrive, I'm not gonna have an active part, just watch and laugh me little bollocks off. Me bollocks that were in severe pain until I ate all these drugs.

After a few more happy people came and relieved me of some of my medicine, I sat down alongside one of the girls who was falling asleep on the seats. How she was falling asleep with the music this loud, I'll never know. But she was.

I looked down at my watch. Quarter to ten. My heart's pounding a little more now. Only fifteen minutes till they get here. *What if it goes pear-shaped? Stop it, Gaz. You're gettin' paranoid, that's all. It won't go pear-shaped.*

Spoke too soon!

A great crash sounded at the side of me, broken glass showering down from above, all over my sleeping friend.

I jumped up. 'What the fuck was that?' Where had it come from? I looked up above the seats and there was an elevated pathway behind them. On the pathway were three guys I'd never seen before. They were laughing and breaking bottles for fun, then kicking them down onto the seats. I could tell looking at them that they were out for trouble. My friend was awake now, cut slightly from the tiny shards of glass in her cheek. She was ranting and raving like a woman possessed. *Fuck.* I don't need this, man. Steve'll be 'ere in five minutes and it's gonna kick off *now.* I looked across the room and noticed some of the bouncers arriving that had done me over. *Fuck.* C'mon, Steve. Where the fuck are ya?

CRASH! More glass comes flying down. These cunts are kicking it all over with no regard for anyone. I turn and stare at the biggest one of the three, the Charlie getting the better of me.

'C'mon, fellas, pack it in. We're all trying to have a good time 'ere. Leave it out.'

I think I was quite genial the way I asked them to stop. The big one then put his arms around his friends, leaned forward, sneered and shouted at me:

'And what the *fuck* are *you* gonna do about it? Ya little cunt!'

It was at this point that I knew they meant business, they weren't gonna leave it. I had no option now. They were gonna do me in. I had to use *reasonable* force, *pre*self-defence, just as Steve had taught me. I lunged at him and cracked my full bottle of Budweiser clean over his skull. The bottle smashed into a million pieces. It felt as though his head did too. A stream of blood squirted from the top his head as he fell to his knees, screaming like a baby. His mates were offskis. Ha. What sort of mates were they? In my drugged and drunken state I didn't even attempt to leave, I just stood there dancin' like I thought I was some kind of superhero. The girls thought I was too. I'd just got rid of the pests. The tall one was still writhing on the floor clutching his skull as though he was holding his head together. Get up, you tosser, it's only a flesh wound.

I looked at my watch. Five to ten. C'mon, Steve. Where are ya?

You know when sometimes you look back, and you wish you'd done something differently? Well, this was one of those times. Hindsight is a wonderful concept. I wish that:

    a) I'd fucked off home as soon as I cracked
        me Bud over that cunt's crust; or
    b) I'd never gone out in the first place.

It all happened so quick. The night before replayed all over again. The bouncers descended on me like the Zulus at Rorke's Drift. They used my head as a battering ram again. Only this time they threw me into an office with the manager and some other staff wandering around. Good. I'm not gonna get me knackers kicked even more inside me guts than they already are. Then it dawned on me. I'm in the office. They're gonna call the feds. I'm gonna do the *Big Bitch*. I can't go to jail, man, I'm not like Unsolved Steve who's in and out the Big House more than his own house. Fuck, they're gonna call 'em.

And they did.

They called the law.

Then one of the fuckers from last night's demolition job on me bollocks gave me a jab to my jaw so that I wouldn't run away. Knocked me clean out.

It was about five minutes later when I came back around. I was still on the office floor in Asia. The police hadn't yet arrived. I was completely out of my face. Obliterated. There were three meatheads stood towering over me.

I looked up at them and said, 'Fuckin'ell. You cunts are *ugly!*'

That was it. They pulled me to my feet and one of them, a real tall but skinny fucker, just pressed my neck and did some mad ninja thing that doesn't hurt but sends you back to sleep again. I was fucked after that.

The next time I woke up I was in a police cell. It was Sunday morning at 10.50am.

My head was fuzzy as fuck. But not fuzzy enough to not understand the charge.

Malicious wounding with intent. Carries a sentence of five years in jail.

One of my worst fears had come to fruition.

I had turned into *Steve.*

CHAPTER SEVEN

—

BEST MATES

AND GOD SAW THE LIGHT,
AND SAW THAT *IT WAS GOOD*

Genesis 1:4

13TH JULY 1985 — AGED 18

They say that there is a time in everyone's life when you turn the corner, a defining moment if you will. When you escape from the confines of childhood and become a man. A moment when your whole outlook on the world is completely changed forever. Today was that day.

Unless of course you count the time way back in 1978 when, at the tender age of eleven, I first saw Debbie Harry burst onto the screen wearing nothing but a tee-shirt.

Mmmmmmmmmmmm.

Today was that day for the simple reason that, not only was it the day when Live Aid was transmitted and everybody in the world tuned in, or that it was the first time I ever told my girlfriend, Jenny, that I loved her, it was also the day that I did my first ever night on the decks.

Nothing on God's green earth could prepare me for the metamorphosis I was about to undergo.

It was the night that I became DJ Gaz.

4:07PM

'I absolutely *love* Bryan Ferry, Jen...' I peeped over Jenny's shoulder as we kissed and cuddled on the sofa. We were watching Live Aid at her house and Bryan Ferry had just walked on stage, 'But not as much as I love you...'

It was the first time I'd ever told anyone that I loved them.

Apart from me mam.

Jenny was my baby. We'd been going out for a good three years now. I'd had the odd fling with other girls when I first started seeing her, but now, nothing could get in the way of me and *my* Jenny. She was, like I say, my baby.

She whispered back that she loved me too and all seemed well in the world. Bryan was doing his thing, Saint Bob Geldof was making millions for the starving in Ethiopia and I had a girl who loved me. We melted into the sofa and kissed some more.

'Gaz...' Jenny pushed herself up from me into a press-up position, 'you know I love you... a lot... and I know that you love me... but...'

Oh no man, she was gonna chuck me, I could sense it. She's just told me that she loves me and now she's gonna break my poor little heart. I couldn't stop myself from putting on a sad face and, 'You're not gonna chuck me, are ya?'

She smiled in the sweetest way, stroked my face and giggled, 'No! Silly. Course I'm not gonna chuck ya, yer daft prat. I love ya, don't I?'

My heart jumped back into gear after the sinking feeling from five seconds ago. Good, I'm not gonna get blown out. Whatever she says now will be wonderful. No matter *what* it is.

'Gaz, I love ya, and I want to be with ya forever, for the rest of me life. But you've been with *loads* of different girls…' I hadn't, I'd only been with about six or seven, but I did have a reputation as a bit of lady-killer, '…and I've only ever been with you. That's good, coz I love ya, but I often wonder what it would be like to go with someone else. Y'know what I mean?'

I was horrified, man.

'Y'mean ya wanna *shag* someone else?'

She shook her gorgeous head furiously, 'No no no, I don't *want* to shag someone else. I just *wonder* what it would be like, that's all. That's all. I'm not gonna go wi' no-one behind yer back or owt. I never would.'

Although I was mortified, I could understand what she meant. How was she expected to only go with me for the rest of her life? I'd had some experience of other people, so why shouldn't she?

I had an alarming brainwave.

'Right then, Jen, just to show ya that I really love ya I'm gonna sort it out for ya to shag someone else. How's that sound? How do fancy shagging my mate Mel? He'll be up for it, I know he will. You're gorgeous so why wouldn't he? Eh, what do ya say to that idea? Then you've got it out of your system and we can carry on being in love. *Forever.*'

Now, seeing as Jenny was so sweet and gorgeous and beautiful and innocent, I knew full well that she wouldn't accept this ludicrous offer. She'd just shrug it off as stupid and I'd look as though I was a really nice, understanding bloke for saying it in the first place. Nah, she wouldn't accept. No way.

'Yeah. Why not? It'll be fun. He's very handsome is Mel. Gorgeous blue eyes. Yeah, good idea, Gaz. Sort it out. Soon.'

She had the cheesiest, dirtiest grin on her face, really excited about the prospect of shagging me best mate. I could have sworn I saw her lick her lips. *Fuck.* I wish I hadn't said a word now. I felt sick. The apparent ease with which she accepted this somewhat ridiculous offer was, what shall I say, *unsettling*, to say the very least.

'Er… right then… I'll phone Mel and sort it out.'

At that I jumped up, did my lovely hair and made my way out of her house and back to The Fanny. For my first ever night as a DJ.

13TH JULY, 7PM

I sat staring through the television. Live Aid was still on but I wasn't listening to it, I was just staring. The butterflies in my stomach must have weighed two stone each. I had to be a DJ in half an hour. How the fuck was I gonna pull that off? I'd never touched any record decks in my life before. I'd never spoken over a microphone. And I only had twenty records.

Fuck, Dad, what *have* you done?

You see, up till tonight my dad had always had live music in the pub. Irish singers and folk groups and the such. But for the past few months the clientele had started to get younger. So, in his infinite wisdom, last week my dad announced to me, 'We need a DJ, son. What do you think? For the young 'uns that are coming in these days.'

It was a good idea. A DJ would make a great change from the leprechauns we'd had murdering *The Fields of Athenry* recently.

And it'd attract the girls too. I agreed with him. It was a *fantastic* idea.

'Good then…' He gave me a knowing wink. 'You start next Saturday. OK?'

I nearly hit the floor. *Fuck* that, man. No way. I didn't think he meant me. I shook my head and said no what must have been a thousand times. But he had ways of being persuasive did me dad.

'Ah c'mon, Gaz, you'll be great. You know all about the music for starters, you have a gift for the blarney that only I could match and, *and* I'll give you thirty pound a night, Saturday and Sunday. If it's a success I'll have you working Fridays too. And, Gazzy boy… you won't *ever* have to serve behind the bar again. Oh…and all the girls'll love you even more than they already do. Girls *always* love the DJ. C'mon, whaddya say? Do it, Gaz. You'll like it, I promise ya.'

That was it. He'd twisted my arm. Bloody hell, it was sixty to ninety quid a week, on top of me day job at the council offices. That only paid me a measly forty-nine quid a week and I had to work bastard forty hours for that. I had no bills with living in The Fanny. The money tempted me. But the *girls* was the one that really did it. I know I was in love with Jenny and all, but adoration from every girl that would ever enter the pub was too much for me to resist. I wouldn't stray from Jenny of course, but the attention would be nice.

So I agreed. The next day, off he went and bought me some second-hand decks and a crappy old microphone. If it took off he said he'd get me some better gear. It better take off, this stuff is bleedin' ancient. I nearly thought I was gonna have to wind them up like a gramophone.

7.15PM

'C'mon down, Gaz, there are people *pouring* into the pub, they must have seen the posters. C'mon,' my dad shouted me from the bottom of the stairs as I sat petrified in the flat above, my head in my hands, heart pounding away.

People *pouring* in. Oh no, man, I can't do it. I'll make a right twat of myself. I felt sick again. He'd put posters up all over the pub announcing "The Newest and Most Talented Star DJ to EVER grace the record decks. They call him Gaz… DJ Gaz… A Legend in the making!"

Nice poster, Dad. I've got *nothing* to live up to with that scrawled all over the place, have I? I rushed to the bathroom and threw up everywhere. I wish my Jenny was here, she'd look after me. She had some sort of family do to go to, so couldn't be with me.

Pull yourself together, Gaz. I placed a hand on my hip, sprayed on some Kouros by Yves Saint Laurent, straightened my jet black quiff, adjusted the collar on my silk paisley shirt, looked in the mirror, blew myself a kiss and said, 'Get yerself downstairs, you clown. Go on stage and *knock their fuckin' socks off!*'

Then I wiped some sick off me chin and swaggered downstairs.

7.30PM

The place was packed out when I got down there – must have been a hundred and fifty people in. Fuck.

I grabbed myself a pint of Guinness and a double brandy and strutted over to the decks.

There was a huge gang of girls sitting right in front of my equipment. Right stunners. I can't fuck up. I just can't. I'll never be able to go out in public again. *Ever!*

I dimmed the house lights and switched on the turntables, my hands shaking like jelly as I placed my first disc on the mat. I picked up the microphone and held it up to my mouth, everyone looking at me. Fuck. What do I say? What do I do? Please God… please help me, I promise I'll go to Mass more often.

I flick the deck switch and the music blasts out from the speakers, it was the opening electronic gymnastics of *You Spin Me Round* by Dead or Alive, an excellent choice of opening song, Gaz. Raucous and engaging, just what the girls wanna hear. I put the mic back down. I hadn't said a word. What the *fuck* was I supposed to say? Everybody was singing along and seemed to be having a good time, drinking and chatting and dancing about, but I would have to say something at some point. I've only got twenty records and they'll only take an hour or so to play before I have to start repeating them. These people need entertaining. The only person that can do that is me. I was dancing along to the song, making shagging movements and pointing to the girls and grabbing my crotch every time it got to the bit about coming section. They seemed to like what I was doing. They could listen to the jukebox though, if all they just wanted to do was hear music all night. I needed to say something. Something entertaining. Something *funny*.

There were about thirty seconds left to play of Dead or Alive.

Then, as if I'd been hit by a thunderbolt of inspiration from the heavens, it came to me. Forget the old routine employed by all the other DJs, the routine that involves announcing the name of the singer and the song, the routine that asks people to come for requests. How could I ask people to come for a request that I would most definitely not have in my grossly underequipped collection? No, I had to do something different.

Take the piss out of people.

Would it work? Was I gonna finish my DJing career as soon as the first record I ever played had finished? Would I get killed by the customers? No time to think, the last chord of the song played, I pulled the microphone up to my grinning face and...

'There you go, kids...' I had a kind of mid-Atlantic drawl in my voice that I'd heard other DJs using all the time, real cheesy. 'Welcome to The Fanny, I'm Gaz and if you've got any requests...' I suddenly shouted in the broadest Yorkshire accent that I could muster, *'KEEP THEM TO YER FUCKIN' SELVES! IT'S MY DISCO AN' I'LL PLAY WOT I BASTARD WANT!'*

I pushed the switch to let the next song start and looked for the reaction around the room. I was overjoyed. People were killing themselves laughing, the girls, the guys, my mam, the bar staff. My dad was shaking his head in disbelief but laughing all the same. I'd just told everyone to go fuck themselves, more or less, and they thought it was hilarious. The girls were looking at me and smiling and winking. I felt as though I was the bee's knees, man. The dog's bollocks. I continued in the same vein throughout the night. I got more confident after each song I played, after each comment I made, after making the whole pub laugh. I took the piss out of people's clothes, their hair, their faces, the way they walked, their choice of partner, anything.

And guess what? They loved it.

They loved me.

A little trick that I employed to ensure that I didn't get my cheeky little head kicked in was to not only take the piss out of the punters, but to take the Mick out of myself too. To show that whatever I said was meant in fun. I called myself a skinny twat and a little bastard, y'know the score.

The end of the night came and as I played out my final record – *New York, New York* – the place was heaving and the entire pub was on its feet dancing. The music went down and I was given a rapturous round of applause. I stood glassy eyed – I'd downed quite a few brandies – and revelled in my triumph. I felt like a *star*.

Two of the girls who had been sat at the tables in front of my decks all night came over to me as I began to unplug my equipment. One of them was extremely beautiful and her mate was pleasant to the eye but not quite as stunning. I'd never seen them before tonight. Both were extremely pissed.

'Gaz, you were ace tonight.' The stunner slurred this into my ear as her friend nodded furiously. 'What yer doin' now that you've finished?' She smiled at me when asking and gave me a super sexy wink. Oh man, I'm in there.

She purred at me, 'You can come with us if you want, we both need shagging.' She giggled, as did her friend, who didn't say anything, just nodded and giggled some more.

I can't believe this, man. My dad said that the girls would love me, but this is too much. Am I dreaming? Two that go together, fuckin' hellfire.

My dad walked past me collecting the glasses and gave me a nod, a nod that said "*See?*" Then he sauntered off, shouting at people to sup up and fuck off.

So here I am, two shag-happy girls, gagging for it, bleedin' kissing my ears and shit as I'm trying to clear my equipment, and what do I do? This is what I do…

'Not tonight, ladies, I'm afraid.' What the fuck am I saying? 'I can't, girls, as sweet and beautiful as you both are. I'd love to, trust me I'd love to, but I've got a girlfriend…' I pulled a mock sad face at them. 'Sorry, ladies.'

They just drunkenly shrugged their shoulders and wandered back to their friends at the table. The stunner turned her head back to me and shook her head, licking her lips, real porno style. I must have been crackers. I couldn't do it though, I couldn't cheat on Jenny. Bloody hell, I'd only told that I loved her this afternoon. She wants to shag Mel, I know, but that's not the same. I love Jenny. And that's it. Simple. No other girls for me. *Ever.*

I'll tell you what though…

I love being *DJ Gaz.*

14TH JULY — THE NEXT DAY

'She wants me to shag her? You are *kiddin*'?' Mel was amazed at what I'd just proposed.

'Yep…' I tried to reassure him that I wasn't having him on, that it wasn't some kind of Gaz joke. 'I'm tellin' yer, man, she hasn't shagged anyone else before so we arranged it for you to shag her. Why not? Yer me best mate, aren't yer? I'll even watch. I might squeeze one off while yer shaggin her.' I laughed at my last comment even though I wasn't entirely sure about the whole situation. But if it would stop Jenny from going off with another bloke, then why not?

Mel laughed out loud, he couldn't believe his luck, he was gonna get a free shag, just like that. From my beautiful, sweet, sweet Jenny.

We arranged to go to the park that night in my car, all three of us. Mel and Jenny would get in the back seat whilst I remained in the front, keeping an eye out. And to see that he didn't "damage" her too much. I didn't want her to be "ruined", did I?

We picked Jenny up from her house at about eight that night. It was still light, being the middle of summer and all. We drove to the park in my Mini, a little black one that my dad bought me for my eighteenth birthday a few months ago. We didn't say very much to each other – it was a really strange situation to be in, and we were all nervous to say the least. We arrived at the park and drank a couple of bottles of Thunderbird between us. Thunderbird makes you pissed. That's all I can say about it. I don't even know what it is. Cider? Beer? Lager? Fuck knows, it just gets you pissed. The more pissed we got the less nervous we became. The sun started to go down and the park began to empty.

We were sitting on the grass outside the car chit-chatting away in the half-lit summer dusk when:

'C'mon then, let's get down to it.'

Jenny jumped to her pretty little feet and placed her hands on her hips as she barked her order. She opened the car door and climbed into the back seat. As she did, she let her skirt hitch up to reveal that she wasn't wearing any knickers. We both got a flash of her bare backside. Her lovely, smooth, untouched by anyone else but me, backside. Fuck. That's not like my Jenny. My sweet, sweet Jenny. Mel looked at me and said:

'Gaz man, do you really want me to do this? I won't, you know. Not if you don't want me to.'

I had a terrible, sad, sinking feeling in me, a feeling that it was now inevitable, that we'd come too far.

Jenny shouted from the back of the car, 'C'mon, stop fuckin' about, Mel. Get in here and shag me.'

She was clearly pissed out of her box. Mel and myself got up from the grass and looked into the car. Fuckin' hell, Jenny was laid out on the back seat, legs wide open, as naked as the day she first got her peachy little arse smacked by a midwife. The mucky bastard. My beautiful, lovely, sweet, angelic Jenny. Legs a-fuckin-kimbo.

I stood open-jawed as she beckoned Mel into the car with her index finger, mouthing the words 'C'mon' to him.

He looked at me again, kind of half smiled and said, 'Are you sure, Gaz?'

Still with my chin on the grass I reluctantly said, 'Yeh, go on, man, she's gaspin' for it.'

'Wahey…' Mel started to rip his trousers off, 'thank fuck for that, Gaz. I've got a *right* hard on, man. A fuckin' cunt buster!' And he dived in the back of the car with Jenny.

I sat in the front and turned on the radio. *I Feel Love* came on, the old Donna Summer disco classic, but it wasn't by her, it was Bronski Beat, a kind of souped-up '80s version. Pretty funky, as it goes. I nodded away to the music as I tried not to look in the rear-view mirror to see what was happening in the back. I could hear all kinds of squelching and slapping and groaning. My sweet little Jenny telling Mel 'that's the hardest cock ever!' Fuckin' hell, Gaz, what are you doin'? You're sat in the front of your car while yer best mate's *butchering* your bird in the back seat. It was too much for me to bear. I had to turn round and look. Aw fuck, now I wish I hadn't bothered. There's Mel, proper annihilating my poor little Jenny, real porno style, pounding away like a bastard jackhammer. Fuckin' hell. I can't stand it. It's too horrible. It's pure *destruction!* They're oblivious to my watching them, they're too caught up in… *that!* I cough to try and get their attention. No. Too busy shagging like bastard dogs. I can't bear to look anymore so I jump up and out of the car, slamming the door as hard as I can behind me, y'know, to let them know I've gone. If they even care.

I march away from my little Mini, head swirling. Fuck. Fuck. Fuck. Jenny's getting *ruined.*

After I'm about twenty-five yards away I hear Jenny coming out from the car and trying to catch up, still bollock naked, trying unsuccessfully to pull her clothes on.

She shouts, 'Gaz, Gaz, are you alright? What's wrong?'

I stop in my tracks and turn to her, my eyes filled with tears.

'What's *wrong*? What's *fuckin'* wrong? Ha. I can't believe you have to ask. What's wrong? Fuckin''ell, Jen. I've just watched you gettin' shagged half to death by me best mate and you ask what's *wrong.* Fuck off, I don't wanna know yer, ya fuckin'…' I'm shaking my head and growling, thinking of something to call her, something to make her feel the way I was feeling. 'Just fuck off away from me, you fuckin' *slag!* Fuck off.'

I started to march back to the car where Mel was being extremely sheepish, saying nothing at my outburst.

Jenny was in tears now, and she screamed to me, 'But it was *your* idea. Not mine. It wasn't my idea. I love *you.* I'm not a slag.'

She fell to her knees and sobbed into her hands. Naked.

I climbed into the driver's seat of the car and revved up the engine. The song on the radio was *Easy Lover* by Phil Collins, fuckin' charmin'. Mel fake coughed from the back seat to get my attention. I turned to him with my face like stone.

He whispered, 'You're not mad at me, are ya, Gaz?' His bright red, sweating head was bowed when he spoke.

My stony features turned into a smile, then I laughed and said, 'Course I'm not mad at yer. Yer me best mate, aren't yer? I'd have done the same if I got it offered on a plate. That's what blokes do. It's not your fault, mate. It's hers…' I stick my head out of the window and shout to a weeping Jenny knelt on the grass, 'her fuckin' fault. The slag!'

I leaned into the back, grabbed Mel around his shoulders and gave him a hug.

Then we drove home.

Without Jenny.

To think, the day before I'd had it offered on a plate by two girls, not one, two, and refused them because I loved Jenny. Well, she can fuck off. I've made my mind up.

Women are twats. Who wants to fall in love anyway? Not me. I'm DJ Gaz.

Super-fuckin-star.

And I'm gonna fuck 'em all. Every last one.

CHRISTMAS 1996 — AGED 29

'You'll do it standin' on yer head, Gaz man. You'll only get two year or summat. It's easy. A piece a piss.' Unsolved gulped the last part of his pint down as he tried to reassure me that prison wasn't too bad. 'It's just an inconvenience,' he said. 'You might even get off, man. You always do, you're a right lucky cunt. Always come up smelling of roses. C'mon, let's go for a drive, matey.'

He picked up his keys and we walked out of the pub to his car. There was a freezing chill in the air.

'Fuck me, Stevie boy, it's brass bastard monkeys out 'ere.' I rubbed my hands and blew into them as we got into the motor. 'Where we off to anyway?'

Steve didn't answer me straight away. He started the car and drove for about two minutes, humming to himself, not a tune, just humming. Then he piped up…

'We're off to pick up a package off Mick the Human. He owes me.' He said this as though he had some kind of unfinished business. Business that I knew would not be to my liking. At all.

I laughed. 'Mick the fuckin' *Human?* Who's he? How come every fucker we know has got a mad nickname? Except for me. The Human? Fuckin''ell, what is he? Everyone's a fuckin' human, ya mad twat.' I was giggling like a girl, muttering 'human' as I laughed.

Steve laughed too. 'Aw, Gaz man, I don't know. They all call 'im it. It's just his nickname, innit? It's funny, I suppose. Anyway, you *have* got a nickname.'

I was intrigued. I never thought I had a nickname. DJ Gaz maybe, or one of the ridiculous stage names that I'd used over the years?

'Have I? What is it?'

Steve turned to me from the driver's seat and whispered something that I couldn't make out.

'Eh? What is it? I didn't hear yer, man. Speak up, yer whispering old twat.'

He laughed a little and then raised his voice.

'It's Gaz the *CUNT.* Ya cunt.' At which he nearly pissed and shit himself laughing.

I was bemused. 'Funny fucker, aren't ya. Gaz the Cunt. Very funny.'

Still laughing he managed to say, 'Nar, mate, I'm only messing wi' yer. It's not Gaz the Cunt. It's Fast Gaz. That's what they're all callin' yer. Fast Gaz.'

I smiled a little. 'Well, it's better than Gaz the fuckin' cunt, I suppose. Fast Gaz? What do they call me that for? I've not had anyone call me it before. First I've heard about it. Fast Gaz?'

'They all call yer it, Gaz man. Even me when yer not about. It's nowt bad, it's just coz yer always fucked out of yer head, man. Always whizzing yer bollocks off on phet. Dashing about all over the shop, man. You never stop buzzin', always in a good mood an' that. Whizzing yer tits off. That's all, man. Nowt bad.'

There was never a truer word spoken. I was always speeding me nuts off, morning, noon and now. I didn't much care for the Charlie. I still took it now and again, but I preferred to slam loads of whizz down my Gregory Peck. Fast Gaz, eh? Could be worse, I suppose.

I was puzzled though. 'How come you 'ant got a nickname like that then, Stevie baby? You're worse than me. You're always at it as well, Charlie an' everything, man. Miles worse than me.'

He looked at me again and whispered, just so that I could hear him this time, 'That's coz I've got a nickname already. I'm Unsolved Steve. And that, my son, is a *scary* nickname. Just the way I want it. I've never killed no cunt, honest. But if cunts wanna believe that I have, then let 'em. Ha!'

He turned back to look at the road in front of him and started humming his no tune song again. We drove for a mile or so heading towards Mick the Human's gaff, talking bollocks as we went.

'Have you ever noticed, Stevie boy, that wherever there's a posh area there's always a poor area next door?'

Steve chuckled. 'Whaddya mean?'

'I mean what I just said. Fool. It's true. Look around Leeds, or any city for that matter, and you'll see what I mean. If you go to a rich area with nice houses and nice cars and that, there's always a poor area within a mile radius. An estate or run-down area where every cunt's a dealer or a smack head or summat. Just look around you, man. They do it on purpose, I swear.'

Steve's intrigued now. 'Who? Who does it on purpose? Does what on purpose?'

'Them! The government. The council. Them cunts. The builders. I don't know. Just them. The powers that be. What they do, Stevie man, is they build lovely big posh houses with tree-lined boulevards and lovely driveways, then they build a council estate nearby. On purpose. Or they build a lovely area close to an already dilapidated area. On purpose. They do. I'm tellin' yer, man, they're cunts for it.'

Steve looks across to me as he's driving. 'Why on earth would they do it on purpose? Ya nutter. They do it wherever they can buy land. Don't they?' He appears unsure.

I proceed with my "theory". 'Nah, man, my theory is this. They do it on purpose. They do it to make cunts jealous. Then when cunts get jealous of what they see all around them, they turn to crime. So that they can have the nice shit an' that.'

Steve's laughing again. 'You must be wrong, Gaz man. Why the fuck would they want people to be fuckin' jealous? They wanna cut crime, man. Not make it go up, you fool.'

I get real serious now. 'Do they fuck wanna cut crime, man. Oh yeah, they bring out these figures every now and again about crime fallin' an' shit. But who believes them? How can they prove it? They can't, can they? We just have to take their word for it, don't we? No, man, they do it on purpose to make people jealous. Without crime there'd be no coppers, would there? No crime, there'd be no lawyers, no judges, no fuck all. They're not gonna make all those bastards out of jobs, are they? No, are they fuckers like, man. They love crime, man. They want crime to increase. On purpose. So that there's summat for all the judicial cunts to do. That's what I think anyway.'

Steve's nodding now, seeming to be in agreement as we turn into an affluent suburb of Leeds, close to the airport.

I didn't know Mick the Human from Adam and the Ants, but when we pulled up outside his house I wanted to know him. It was a fucking mansion, man. Huge fucker, great big ornamental steel gates with electronic security and all that bollocks. Impressive. Steve had to speak into a thing on the gatepost in order for them to open. Once through the gates there was a long, winding, tree-lined drive up to the house. Like the Road to Mandalay.

'Fuck me, Steve man. Look at this gaff. What the fuck does he do? It must have twenty bedrooms, man.' I was in awe of the sight before me. It reminded me of Hugh Hefner's place, the Playboy gaff.

Steve was grinning like the cat that got the cow, forget the cream.

'This, Gaz… is bastard Disneyland.'

We got out of the Beamer and walked up the drive to the door. We could hear loud music and laughing and singing from the windows. It sounded packed. Steve knocked on the door. It was Clockwork John who opened it, a James Brown song pumping through the door, *I Feel Good*.

'Come into the parlour said the spider to his flies.' Clockwork winked his mascara eyelash at us as he said this. He sounded scary to me.

Steve just laughed and pushed past him, grabbing my arm and pulling me in. The entrance hall was like a hotel lobby. It was enormous, a great golden staircase before us. I thought I was in Hollywood, man. Real *Scarface* shit. What a place. There were people everywhere. Not the kind of fuckers you get in Mad Marko's gaff, scraggs and cunts. No. These were beautiful people. Supermodel girls swanning around, millionaire looking dudes swanning round the girls. Champagne seemed to be in everybody's hands. Handsome men bobbing their heads to the music. It was a good place. I could tell. The people were nice, girls were coming up to us with Champers and cocaine, the guys were telling us to get whatever we wanted from the bar. A good place. I could get used to this.

Then Clockwork John appeared again, wearing a white boiler suit. I could see a little speck of blood on his sleeve.

'Hi de hi de hi there, droogs. Have I got a surprise for you two little beastie boys. Come with Uncle, you are invited.'

He turned to the golden staircase and waved at us to follow him. We grabbed a bottle of Moet & Chandon each from the bar and walked after him.

At the top of the stairs we walked along a corridor. The walls were lined with works of art, paintings of Jesus and what have you. Fuck knows who they were by, but they looked expensive. We got to a room at the end of the corridor. John opened the great oak door and beckoned us in. He walked straight in and sat down on a red leather Chesterfield sofa, saying nothing. We followed. As we got around the great oak door, I stood in disbelief. I froze. Before me were two men tied to chairs, their arms around the back. They had red pillowcases tied over their heads, their bowed heads. They were moving slightly and groaning. What the fuck have we walked into? I turned to Steve, sweating, my heart about to implode. He looked nervous as he stared back at me, then he smiled, laughed out loud and shouted:

'SURPRISE!'

Three other guys came in to the room, all laughing and shouting surprise too. Steve put his arm around me and sat me down on another Chesterfield, all the while *Do You Wanna Funk?* was playing downstairs but we could still hear it real loud up here. Of the three guys who came in, two of them, real mean looking fuckers, walked over to the tied up blokes and stood either side of them. They were still groaning. The other guy, about my size, he looked Italian or Spanish or something, came and sat with me and Steve. He leaned over and put his arms around Steve.

'Hi Steve. Mr Unsolved Steve. I'm glad you could make it to my little soiree. Is this Gaz?' He patted me on my knee as he asked.

Steve lifted my arm up and moved it toward the guy. 'Yeh Mick, this is Gaz. Go on, Gaz. Shake Mick's hand.' I shook the bloke's hand as Steve said, 'Mick the Human, this is Fast Gaz. Fast Gaz, this is Mick the Human. There ya go. Now yerv been introduced.'

I was still shocked at the two blokes tied to the chairs, although it now seemed that I didn't appear to be in any immediate danger.

'What the *fuck* is going on?' I half shouted this question.

They all laughed. Clockwork John in the corner laughed like a mad man.

The Spanish, Italian bloke, who I now knew to be Mick the Human, opened his mouth again. He had a London accent. Not Spanish. Or Italian.

'This is a surprise, Gaz. A surprise for you.'

As he said this, one of the meatheads produced a baseball bat and cracked it right across the front of one of the tied up guy's faces. A little yelp came from within the red pillowcase. The guy at the other side pulled out a bat and cracked it over the top of the head of the other one. No yelp. Just a twitch. As I watched in horror I saw that the pillowcases used to be white – the red was blood. It was soaked completely through the entire case. On both men. It was a small white section showing near where the rope was tied around their necks that gave it away. The two meatheads then began to whack and whack and whack away at the heads of these two poor fellas. They were obviously unconscious inside the pillowcases, but no matter, they still kept being pounded. The music that was playing was *Dancing On A Saturday Night* by Barry Blue. Steve was laughing and singing along to the song as they stoved their heads in for over thirty seconds. Trust me when

I say that it seemed like hours. Clockwork John was doing a kind of Cossack dance in the corner. Nutter. They must have got forty blows a piece. Blood was gushing down both of their necks from inside the pillowcases.

'That's enough now, Milo, enough, Joshua. ' Mick the Human waved his finger at the meatheads to stop. They both looked knackered. It must have taken it out of them. 'Take off their hoods.'

Milo and Joshua pulled off the hoods and pushed the chairs to the ground, each giving the poor unconscious fuckers a kick to the head as they fell.

'Do you recognise these men, Gaz? My new friend Gaz.' Mick the Human was seeming more like Mick the Inhuman as he asked the question.

I was stuttering a little, 'How the fuck am I supposed to recognise them? They're covered in claret, man. And their heads are massive. They won't even recognise their selves in a mirror.'

It was one of the most repugnant sights I had ever had the misfortune to see. The heads of the two guys must have been four times bigger than their natural proportions. They were as big as space hoppers. They were covered in black and red blood. I couldn't make out who they were. They looked like Big Brain Headed Aliens from 1950s science fiction films.

Mick the Human went on to tell me the tale.

'These, Fast Gaz, are two fuckhead bouncers from that shithole of a nightclub, Asia. They are friends of the police, you might say. Stool pigeons, ha ha ha har! Well, look at them now...' He throws his champagne at them laid out on the floor in their own blood. Dead, by the look of it. 'They don't look very fuckin' clever now, do they? We, that is my associates and I, found out that these two maggots were informants, that they were supplying the police with information. Information that I, and my associates, did not care for the police to have. So, my new friend Fast Gaz, here is the result. This…' He points at them and spits a greeny on one of them. 'This is what happens to informants. Grasses. I don't like grasses. I'll kill 'em all. And anyone who looks like them. I'll fuckin' go out and leave 'em where I fuckin' find 'em. Our friend Steve told me that you are a very good friend of his. His best mate. That you had been in some trouble with these cunts also. That you may be going to do some jail time because of them. We told Steve our plan, what we were going to do to these worms, and we asked him to bring you along for the ride. Revenge for us, and for you. Kill two birds with one stone, as it were.'

Clockwork John burst out laughing. 'Ha ha, kill two birds, ha ha ha.' And he walked over to the two pulp-headed messes on the floor and started making bird noises and flapping his arms like wings. Nutter.

Mick the Human stood up and walked across the room to a Chippendale cabinet. He pulled out a huge bag of coke and tossed it to Steve. Must have been a kilo at least.

'Prezzie for ya, Steve man. Merry Christmas. Now, come on, let's go back down and enjoy the party. I have guests to entertain.' He turned to his two meathead minders, pointed to the bodies on the floor and said, 'Get rid of that fuckin' mess. Take them to you know where and do you know what.'

Mick the Human may have been a scary fucker, but he certainly knew how to throw a party. We stayed till the sun came up. Drinking, dancing, drugging, you know the score.

Driving home in a daze, I turned to Steve and mumbled, 'Good night that, man, when all's said and done. I know I shouldn't really but I feel a bit sorry for them bouncer cunts. Don't you?'

'Nah, fuck 'em,' was all I got in reply.

'Ha ha...' I had to laugh at his indifference. 'You still haven't told me why they call him Mick the fuckin' Human. Don't you know? Really?'

Steve shook his head, shrugged his shoulders, then smiled at his bag of Charlie and said,

'Nah, man. I haven't got the first fuckin' clue. He's a good lad though, isn't he?'

I laughed sarcastically. 'Oh yeah. Fuckin' great.'

CHAPTER EIGHT

—

MADRID, ELVIS, JAGGER AND DI

Insomnia– Faithless
(Maxi Jazz, Sister Bliss and Rollo) 1995

SUMMER 1986 – AGED 19

In 1918, the German playwright Bertolt Brecht wrote his earliest play as a twenty-year-old student. The play was called *Baal*. In *Baal*, Brecht created a monster of sensuality and self-gratification, a hedonistic drunkard who was named after a pagan god. Although Baal is not the most handsome of men, he has an ego as large as the moon, he is rude, obnoxious and immoral to the core. Despite these flaws he is irresistible to women. This makes him the envy of men and also admired by them. He sleeps with every woman he ever comes into contact with and abandons them just as easily. In the end he kills his best friend and dies alone in a woodman's cottage.

I had never read the play, but I did see it on the telly in 1982. It starred David Bowie and it was brill. I wanted to be David Bowie. Even more so, I wanted to be Baal.

Except for the part where he kills his mate and dies alone. That bit's not good.

I was a success. In The Fanny at least. I was king of the decks.

DJ Gaz.

The World's Number One DJ and Porno Legend.

This was a name I gave myself of course. I wasn't really the best in the world. But I knew I could be. The Fanny was packed to the seams every weekend now. My dad was making a fortune. And, for my youth, so was I. Nineteen years old, a hundred and forty quid a week! Spot on.

My confidence had grown a thousand fold from the stutterings of my first night. Nothing could stop me. People came from all over Leeds to see me play. To get the piss taken out of them. They loved it. They loved me.

An old friend of my dad's had come into the pub one night while I was playing. He was a DJ also. Pretty famous around Leeds, a legend. He was also called Gaz. Gaz Granville. He was about forty years of age. He was impressed with what he saw and heard and came over to give me his approval. Not only did he tell me how great he thought I was, he gave me a huge box of records. I'd been investing in all the latest tunes over the months, even got some new decks and a new microphone. But the collection that Gaz gave me was massive, just over four hundred singles.

'They're for you, lad. You're on your way up just as I'm on my way out. I won't be needing 'em anymore.' He shook my hand and wished me luck.

I was over the moon. One of the legends of Leeds had passed his crown to me in the best of grace. He probably wished he'd never given me his records though – he was still DJing fifteen years later. He must've had to buy 'em all from scratch again. But he was still a legend.

All was well in the world.

These were the good times.

The best times.

I was always a big-headed get, thinking that I was real handsome and all. I'm not. I just think I am. I'm not bad looking, not unpleasant to the eye, but I'm no shaving advert either. However, if you convince yourself that you're lovely, it's easy to convince everyone else.

The fact that you're the DJ makes you even more handsome than you already think you are. The girls love the DJ, as my dad had told me. He was right. They didn't want me for me though, they just wanted to shag the DJ. Then tell their mates that they'd shagged the DJ. Hell, I'm not bothered what they wanna do. I'll be a piece of meat for any girl. No skin off my nose.

'The trick is, Gaz…' My uncle Georgie was trying to explain women to me. 'The trick is, shag 'em all. Coz if you don't, you might miss a good 'un.'

It was an excellent piece of advice.

And I took it. With brass knobs on.

If they threw themselves at me, who was I to complain?

The best thing is, they never wanted anything more than a quick tumble, no strings, no dinners, no fuck all. They came in all ages, shapes, sizes. Tall women, small women, young women, older women, single mothers, married women, divorced women, blondes, brunettes, redheads. You name it. No fatties though. My rule was, 'If I can't lift them above my head, they're not coming in my bed.'

It was fantastic. I was addicted.

I thought back to my Jenny, sweet, sweet Jenny. She'd created a monster. She'd created Baal.

One Saturday night when I was playing, a bouncer from the local nightclub, Madrid, came into The Fanny. He was standing at the bar for a while with his mate, all the while looking over at me. Then they started to march over to the decks. At first I thought, *Aw fuck!* Was he gonna stove me cake in? Had I shagged his bird in Madrid? I did go in there quite often after work and there was always someone wanting a piece of DJ Gaz. Half the time I didn't even know their name, let alone who their boyfriend might have been.

Had some jealous boyfriend sent him to kill me?

There were a lot of girls in that night. I knew I'd be able to take my pick later on. But not if I got bitch kicked all over the pub by two fatheads.

There was one girl in particular that I was instantly drawn to. She was the most beautiful creature I had ever seen, just like Bardot. She was with a fella, one of the local gangster types, and she had her head bowed, as though she was constantly checking her shoes or something. Katie Farmer was her name. I saw her peek up a couple of times, right into my line of sight, and then look back towards the floor in case her fella spotted her looking. She was gorgeous. I remember thinking in my head, *She will be mine... Oh yes... She will be mine.* But I had these meatheads to contend with for now. Katie could wait.

I had Diana Ross playing on the decks – *Chain Reaction*.

The Madrid guys both stopped in front of me and the bouncer put out his big tree trunk hand for me to shake it.

'Hi, I'm Eddie. Gaz, isn't it?' He sounded friendly enough, huge, bulging bastard but friendly all the same.

The record was just about to finish so I stuck my headphones on to cue in and I waved my finger at him as if to say 'one sec while I change songs'. They were both wearing little vests, showing all their muscles off, like bodybuilders always do. But it was freezing outside. It was July, but it was still freezing. I picked up the mic, nervously looking around at the crowd then back at the two brutes in front of me. Here goes nothing.

'There you go, ladies and gents, good old Diana giving it plenty. Are you all having a good time?'

The crowd all shouted *YEAH!*

'Good. I've got a great show for ya tonight. Looking around the room I see we've got some gorgeous people in. Gorgeous girls, guys, bar staff, everyone. Just take a look at these two fine meaty specimens, ladies...' I point to the two steroid heads in front of me, a few of the girls wolf whistle at them and they both look really shy. 'They really are big lads, eh? But what the *FUCK* is with those vests? It's freezing outside. Freezing. You two guys have either come in a car or you're both as hard as nails...' I look at them both, smiling. 'Nah, they must have come in the car! Soft *bastards!*'

At this, I cranked up the next song, *Rebel Yell* by Billy Idol, and took a big, fuck off swig of brandy. The two guys looked at me menacingly and then laughed. Everyone else in the room laughed too. Good, they took it in fun. Thank fuck. My dad was shaking his head behind the bar as usual.

I held my hand out again to shake. 'Yeh, Gaz is me name. Eddie, did ya say? I didn't upset ya both then, did I? I were only messin' about. What canna do for ya boys?'

Eddie came closer, around the back of the decks so that I could hear him over the music.

'Nah, mate, yer okay. It were funny. We love yer, yer good, man. Yer a good DJ. Best one we've seen in ages. That's why we're 'ere. Our boss sent us up to see yer. From Madrid.'

This is sounding promising. I won't let on that I'm gonna shit myself with excitement. I act real calm.

'Yeah? Go on. Tell me more.'

Eddie puts his arm around me. 'Listen. Our boss has seen yer playing. He thinks yer the business, lad. Everyone who comes into Madrid keeps telling him he should get you to work there. That you're the best. He's asked us to come up and make you an offer. Do you fancy it?'

I was fit to bursting inside. Yes. Yes. Madrid. Think of it, Gaz. One of the biggest nightclubs in Leeds and they want *you* to work there.

'How much is he offering?' I remain calm as I ask the question. I'm not even bothered what the pay is really. It's Madrid, man. I'd work there for free.

'What are yer on now, Gaz?'

I lied, 'Fifty bar a night, Friday, Saturday and Sunday.' My dad gave me thirty a night really.

'Our gaffer says he'll give you a hundred quid a night. Thursday, Friday and Saturday. How's that sound?'

I nearly fuckin' shit meself then and there. A long 'un? Hundred fuckin' quid? A night? Fuck me.

I still acted calm and changed the song over – *Native New Yorker* by Odyssey.

'I can't leave me dad, he's been good to me.' I was ecstatic inside at the prospect of three hundred notes a week.

He put his hand on my shoulder. 'Gaz, mate, you won't have to leave here at all. You can still work for your dad. You won't have to start at Madrid until 11.30pm. You can work here, then come down there after. It's only two minutes away. You finish here at 11pm, don't yer? Job's a good 'un.'

He was right, I could easily make it work.

I took his number and arranged to call him the next day to meet his boss.

Fuckin' hellfire.

Three hundred a week off them, ninety a week off me dad. Three hundred and bastard ninety quid for Thursday to Sunday. Wahey! A few hours a night. Singing, dancing, drinking and shagging.

It's time to give up the day job.

So I did.

My poxy forty-nine quid for forty fucking soul-destroying hours job at the council had to go, man.

Bye bye, council.

Hello wine, women and song.

And hello three hundred and ninety fucking quid a week!

Madrid was the making of me. It was one of the most popular clubs in Leeds. Nearly a thousand people every night. It was a fantastic platform for me to show off my talents. All the other nightclubs in Leeds just had a DJ playing music, which is all well and good I suppose. But Madrid was a "show bar". It had big name acts on stage early on in the evening before the DJ started. Bernard Manning, The Drifters, Edwin Starr, Showaddywaddy. This put the punters in the mood to be entertained even more, not just music and dancing. It was perfect for my brand of "shock jock" frivolity.

There were women everywhere. Centre, right and left.

I was like a kid in a sweetshop, a bull in a china shop and anything else in any other kind of shop.

I carefully cultivated an image to suit my ways. I always had a brandy in my hand, Courvoisier. What else would do? I wore white suits, not harking back to my love of John Travolta and my now effortless strut, more like *Miami Vice*. Pastel tee-shirts and sockless shoes. Sometimes I even wore a Panama hat like the Man from Del Monte. I was often known to stick a few twenty pound notes in the hat rim, just to show off. I involved the audience. I'd shout, they'd shout back. I'd dance, they'd cheer.

I rocked.

The punters loved me. The boss loved me. The bar workers loved me. The bouncers loved me. And best of all… the ladies loved me.

Fuck off, Gaz the Geek.

Bye bye, Gaz the Spod.

See ya later, Gaz the fumbling fool.

Say hello to DJ Gaz – the World's Number One DJ and Porno Legend.

Only this time… it was the truth.

30TH/31ST AUGUST 1997 – AGED 30

Scientists have a name for it, y'know the way that everybody knows exactly what they were doing when someone famous died. I don't know what the scientists call it, but it does have a name. "Something memory". Or something.

Oh yeah, I know. They call it flashbulb memory. Weird, isn't it? You can't remember what you had for your dinner eleven days ago, but you know exactly what you were doing years ago.

It's crazy, man.

My dad always tells me that he can remember what he was doing when he first heard that JFK was killed by the CIA. He says that he was kissing his new girlfriend for the first time, and that she tasted like margarine. So he got rid of her. Charming. He has a go at me for getting rid of a bald lass and he goes around blowing 'em out just because they taste like marge.

I can recall way back in 1977 when Elvis Presley died. Wednesday 16th August. I was just getting off the ferry with my family, coming home from Ireland in the summer holidays. It was mad. We got off the boat and all the Scousers in Liverpool docks were crying their eyes out. As though he was their dad or something. I was only ten, I didn't really give a monkey's fuck.

I'd pretended to my mam that I was too ill to go school the day John Lennon died. Monday 8th December 1980. She believed me, so I got to lie in bed all day listening to the radio. I ended up wishing I'd gone to school. All they did was play bastard Beatles songs. And cry.

They say you never forget the time you first ever meet a mashed-out-of-their-tree Mick Jagger sound-alike as well. Tonight would be that night.

Oh, and it was the night that Princess Diana was killed.

We'd been on a mental session that day, me and Stevie boy. Our heads were on springs, like Zebedee, man. In the town all day and night and then on to Casablanca's at about 2.30am. It was crazy in there, small, dingy, sweaty, loud, full of drugged-up fools not knowing what on earth they were doing. That included me and Unsolved. We were fucked. Just laid out on some beanbags in the chill-out room, talking nonsense to everyone and everybody.

'I can't take it anymore, Steve man. I've gotta get out. I can't handle it.' I was twitching like a motherfucker when I spoke. I was in a good mood but twitchy all the same.

Steve twitched too. 'Nah, Gaz, don't go, man. It's a good laugh in 'ere. Look. It's full of buffoons.' He points at some guys in leather, arseless trousers and chuckles to himself.

I throw another E down my neck and jump to my feet to get lively again.

'No, man. I don't mean I want to get out of 'ere. I mean I wanna get out of the game. The business. It's doin' me head in, Steve man. I don't make any money. Ever. I just eat everything meself and end up owing cunts money...' Steve's nodding in agreement as I continue, 'You're in too deep an' all, Steve. You're gonna get nicked or killed or summat. I'm gonna get sent to the Big House for fuck knows how long. It's just shit, man. I'm fed up with it. I's not normal.'

Steve jumped up and started dancing at the side of me.

'Chill out, Gazzy boy. It's been a long day, that's all. You'll feel better tomorrow. Honest.' He put his arm around me and hugged me up to him. I pushed him off me.

'I feel alright *now*. I feel fuckin' *ace*, man. That's the point. Listen to this. We've lost some good friends this year. Dead. All down to drugs…' My voice is getting louder as I try to make him hear me over the loud house music. 'Alan hung himself after going on a downer after a session on the whizz. Young Graham died in his flat, man, all alone. He took too many Es. Fuckin' hell, Steve man, they say that his blood fuckin' boiled. They didn't find him for five days. Poor cunt. Tony Smedley got his throat slit over a poxy twenty quid deal. John Flake got stabbed, I don't know, fifty fuckin' times in his neck. For fuck all. Coz some cunt was coked up. Sammy Mambo got set on fuckin' fire, for fuck's sake. There's people being shot up all over the fuckin' city. It's no good, man. I'm getting out, before it's too late. I need to settle down.'

Steve laughed, 'It's a good point,' and carried on nodding his head in time to the pumping beats.

I sat back down on one of the beanbags and turned to some completely random stranger, a girl, obviously off her tits. Her jaw was everywhere. Her pupils came outside of her eyes they were that big.

'What do you think?' I asked her, not expecting anything resembling a coherent reply.

'I think, therefore I am.'

I was right. She was a div. Fuck her, she sounds like Mick Jagger.

I looked back up to Steve. He was still dancing. No, more like shuffling. I beckoned to him to come and sit beside me. He did.

'Look, Steve man, I'm getting' out whether you do or not… WOW…' My E had just kicked in – it was a "report to the dance floor" moment. I leapt back to my feet and jumped around like a rabid chimp.

Steve pissed himself laughing and shouted, 'You were saying?' He jumped up and pranced about too. We were mullied. Ah well, you know what they say – sleepin' is cheatin'!

As the song was coming to an end a girl came running into the chill-out room, crying and screaming, 'She's been shot! She's been shot!' She was most upset. Was it her friend who had been shot? Was there a crazed gunman in the club? Then she ran back out again.

I leaned over to the Mick Jagger voice girl and asked, 'Who's been shot? Is someone dead?'

'It's Prince Diane, man… dead as a fuckin' Dodo.' She Jaggered at me, then rolled over and threw up all over her sleeping mate.

Prince Diane? Does she mean Princess Diana? She must do. Fuckin' Prince Diane.

I asked around the room. Everyone was cabbaged. I eventually found out from a bouncer what had happened – he'd been to a petrol station and had heard about the fatal crash in Paris.

Fuckin' shot. These people are mental. Steve's mental. Jagger's mental. I'm going mental. I'm going mental and I'm going home.

I left Steve in his own little world and made my way home.

It was quite upsetting the next day, when I came around a little. When I heard the news properly about the princess. What upset me was the grief that the whole world was feeling, as though she was their mother or sister. It was mad.

The thing that upset me the most though was that Steve got into his car and drove home by himself. I'm usually able to persuade him to get a taxi when he's on Planet 9. But because I'd left him, he drove home.

He drove home and got nicked.

Fuck.

He'll definitely lose his driving licence.

The kilo of coke they found in his car boot won't fuckin' help either.

CHAPTER NINE

—

TOMMY TEN MEN

I Love The Nightlife–
Alicia Bridges – 1978

SUMMERTIME 1987 — AGED 20

When does a boy become a man? It's a difficult one I know, but I have this theory. The male of our species gets to the age of eighteen. And stays there forever. That's my theory.

You get twenty, thirty, forty year olds – inside they're all eighteen. Fuck, even old grandads in their eighties feel eighteen in their heads. It's a fact.

We never grow up is what I'm trying to say. Ask any woman, they'll say the same, and I agree with them. What's the point of growing up? It's shit. If growing up means having to be responsible and boring and all that shit, then stay eighteen. I'm gonna.

So here's me, twenty years of age but still eighteen, not much difference I grant you. But you see, now that my teenage years had gone, I felt that I had to act more like a grown man would. That meant moving out from The Fanny, away from the family and setting up on me own. Why not? I had plenty of cash. I needed some room. The Fanny was great, all the family under one roof. Me, my dad, my mam, my sister, my two brothers, my granny, my two uncles, both of their girlfriends, my sister's boyfriend. And our dog, the drooling bastard that it is. Yeah, The Fanny was great, but the upstairs flat was often as crowded as the pub downstairs. Now, that's all well and good, y'know, good fun. It was real family stuff. All mucking together, helping out the business, having a laugh, playing jokes on each other and that. But when you share a room with four other blokes, and two of them are your little brothers, then entertaining the ladies can get a little… how can I put it? Tiresome? Bothersome? Hard work, to say the least. There's no fun in having to shove a mucky sock in some bird's mouth so that your brothers can't hear her in the throes of passion. Is there? I mean, who wants to kiss her after that? Or having them ask you every morning over breakfast, 'Gaz, were you trying to kill that lady last night? Did you have a poorly willy? Was that lady kissing it better? Why were you bending her over and slapping her bum with your belly?' Fucking hell, I always thought they were asleep. Questions like that from an eleven-year-old and a nine-year-old are too much for any man to bear. It had started to do me Swede in. Time for me to go.

So I did. I upped and went.

I was making good money at the new club. I'd moved on from Madrid to a town centre place, Fat Sally's. One of the many "theme bars" that cropped up in Leeds during the '80s. Irish bars, African bars, American bars, Aus-fuckin'-stralian bars, all sorts, man. This one was a Wild West bar, although the only thing that made it Wild West was the cowboy hats stuck to the ceiling. And a stuffed sealion.

It was lively as hell, it paid well and it was full of women. Available women.

Just my cup of tea.

I became friendly with one of the bouncers, John Flake, or Flakey to everyone else. He was a good bloke, a little bigger than me and harder than a coffin nail. All the girls loved him. Girls always love bouncers. Girls love bouncers and they love DJs. It made perfect sense for me and Flakey to get a place to share. We got a rented house near The Fanny, so that I could be close to the family, go visit them when I wanted. It wasn't a palace, but it wasn't a shithole either. It didn't really matter what it was like, we were gonna Party Harty Marty!

Party central. Vice city.

It was like a bleedin' knockin' shop.

Every single night of the week was like Saturday night for us. Partying till all hours.

Women everywhere. We loved it.

We'd sleep until around 11am, get up, shower, pub for twelve. Drink until 7pm then work until midnight. Flakey on the door, me on the decks. We'd have a collection of girls to choose from at the end of the night, back to ours, and... Party Central. Vice city.

It was fucking *excellent*!

We worked seven nights a week. We didn't mind , it wasn't exactly hard, just tiring. But you know what they say? If you have a job that you love, you'll never work a day in your life.

It did, however, begin to take its toll after about a month of living together in Party Land. We'd just done thirty-three nights insane partying on the trot, and we were goosed.

'Flake man, I'm fucked. I can hardly keep me yoks open.' I was propping myself up against the bar in Fat Sally's. Flake was slouched on a stool beside me, rubbing his eyes and running his fingers through his long black mullet.

'Me too, Gaz man. It's only 5pm and we've gotta work soon. Fuckin' Saturday night, it's gonna get packed out, man. We'll be busier than a bastard.'

Before I came on at seven to do my thing there'd be background music pumping away. *It's A Sin* was on by the Pet Shop Boys. The place was starting to fill up already. There were a couple of hen parties in. We liked the hen parties –always good for a squeeze, especially the hen. There were the usual gangs of fellas being a bit rowdy, doing shots of tequila and grabbing birds' arses. Just an average Saturday teatime in Fat Sally's.

I noticed out of the corner of my tired eye, a guy walk in through the saloon doors and proceed to the other end of the bar from us. He ordered a drink and then sat on his lonesome in a booth, with his legs crossed like a girl and his pinky stuck out from his glass as though he were drinking Earl Grey with the Queen. I thought he looked a real weird fucker. He was suited and booted, but there was summat just not the full shilling about the dude.

I pointed him out to Flakes and said, 'Flakes man, keep yer eye on this fucker in that booth. He doesn't look right, pal.' Flakey looked across, and when he noticed who I was talking about he became super excited.

'Aw, Gaz man, we're sorted. We are *FUCKIN'* sorted, mate. See that guy? I know him. He's cush...' He pointed at the well-dressed weirdo. 'He'll definitely have summat that'll keep us awake and make us lively again.'

'What? What the fuck could make us lively and awake? We've had about ten hours sleep this month. We're both gonna die.' I was curious. Tired and curious.

'He'll have some speed on him. It's good gear an all, keeps you rockin' like fuck.'

Flake was real happy at the prospect of procuring some drugs from this fella. I wasn't so sure though. I didn't particularly agree with drugs – bad mazzle. Sure, I'd had the odd spliff when I was younger, but that didn't do me any favours. I nearly shagged a fat bird on it. The nearest I'd been to drugs after that was when I'd taken some mushrooms, the magic variety, with Mel and a lad called Cocoa a couple of years back. I hated 'em. My body went squishy, I thought I was a jellyfish. Mel sat on the grass on the park. And fell off. Fuck knows how he fell off, the ground was flat as fuck, nowhere to bastard fall, but he fell all the same. Cocoa, well, he just died. He ate a peach while he was off his nut and choked on the stone. He didn't even know that he was choking because his throat had gone numb. He didn't know, and we didn't care. We thought he was messing around. So up until now I'd never even considered touching drugs. Any drugs. But speed would be okay I suppose. It's not like it's heroin or coke. Is it? Yeah, why not? I might as well, I'm fuckin' knackered. I'm knackered and I've gotta work.

And shag loads of girls.

I nodded to Flakey, 'Go on then, man, go over and see him. I daren't speak to him, he looks nuts. Get us some or we're gonna fall asleep stood right here. Will it be okay? It won't fuck us up, will it?'

He gave me a wink and a smile. 'Nah, Gaz man, it'll be cushty, I've had it before. It's sorted. C'mon over wi' me. I'll introduce yer. He's cool, man.'

We strutted over to the weirdo guy and sat opposite him. In the background, Whitney Houston was singing that she wanted to dance with somebody. I sat down feeling a little nervous. I really didn't like the look of this weird fucker, he had dark staring eyes, shark's eyes. He had a bandage on both of his thumbs too. How do you get a bandage on both thumbs? Had he fallen and landed on his thumbs? No, apparently what did happen was, he'd ripped some cunts off for two hundred quid, they hunted him down like a dog, beat him in an alley and broke both of his thumbs for him. Nice. We're dealing with a real charmer here by the sound of it. Proper Errol Flynn. But Flakey knows him, and if Flakey says he's a good lad, then he's a good lad. Flake reached over and shook his hand, taking care not to hurt his bad thumb.

'How are ya, mate? Long time no see. This is me mate Gaz, he DJs here.'

Crazy weirdo guy looked me up and down and kinda whispered, 'Hi Gaz, I'm Steve.' Then he looked back at Flakey. 'I bet I know what you're after. Yer after some Billy, yeah?'

Flake laughed and nodded. Weird Steve pulled out a bag of white powder, chucked it across the table and said, 'Don't eat it all at once, ladies, you'll do yerself an injury.' He then threw what was left of his brandy down his neck, jumped to his feet, straightened his lapels and fucked off. Just like that.

Flakey was happier than Larry now. 'We're sorted, Gaz man, that's us up all night now. No worries. Ha...' Then he put on a Jamaican accent and kinda sung, 'Don't worry, be happy, man.'

I was puzzled by his strange friend just up and leaving like that.

'Yer mate Steve...' I started to pry, 'is he normal? Should I know him? What's his full name? Steve what?'

Old Flakey boy opened the bag of speed before he answered me and shared it, half each emptied into the palm of our hands.

'Go on, Gaz man, down yer neck.' He gulped his down and then mine followed. It tasted fuckin' awful. Like piss. But almost instantly the hairs on the back of my neck stood upright and I got a terrific tingling throughout my body. I like this feeling. I like it a lot. Flake looked over at me and smiled, his body giving a little shiver from the speed. 'Steve's cush, man, he's a real good lad. I've known him for years. Bit of a nutter but he's okay. Do you know, Gaz, I don't even know his surname. He does have a nickname though.'

I felt fuckin' fantastic now, like ten men. 'Yeah? What's his nickname? Weirdo? Ha ha.'

'No, Gaz man, it's Unsolved Steve.'

SEPTEMBER 1997 — AGED 30
WEETWOOD POLICE STATION, NORTH LEEDS

The fat copper sat his huge arse on the crappy aluminium chair and it almost buckled under his eighteen stone of lard.

The shivering suspect laughed out loud at the wobbling cop and muttered under his breath, 'Fat cunt.'

PC Freud wasn't amused. 'I'll give you fat fuck, you fuckin' smack head bastard...' He was not amused at all. He leaned across the table and grabbed the young lad by the throat. 'I fuckin' hate burglars, you little junkie scum cunt. My old mam got burgled, never got over it she didn't. You are goin' down, boy. *DOWN!*' He was shouting, embarrassed by the fact that this scum sucker and his own colleague had watched his fat behind nearly breaking the cheap furniture.

'Look, let's calm down, gents...' PC Humbert intervened. He wasn't fat at all, in fact he was very thin indeed – he looked like a smack head himself. 'We're getting carried away with ourselves.'

He looked over at the suspect. He was a young guy, about eighteen years of age, been brought in on a charge of burgling a chemist. He didn't steal anything. The alarm went off as soon as he got through the window, and he couldn't get back out. And got caught. They're not the brightest people smack heads. They wouldn't be on smack if they were, would they? Paul Ingleby was his name.

'Right, Paul…' PC Humbert shuffled some papers that were on the desk in front of him.

'You've said that you do not want a solicitor present, is that correct?'

Paul the Scrote rubbed his throat where Freud had grabbed him. 'If he keeps grabbing me fuckin' throat pipe, man, I'm sayin' *fuck* all.'

Humbert gave Freud a disapproving glance. 'That won't be happening again, Paul. Will it, PC Freud?' Freud shook his head, grimacing as he did.

'Good…' Humbert reached his hand over and took Paul's in his. 'Right then, Paul, you said that you may have some important information for us, that might make us look at your burglary charge in a more favourable light, so to speak. Is that correct?'

Paul was a rattling, shaking mess. He didn't want to go down for burglary, twelve months at least. How would he get his heroin in the shovel, man? Oh yeah, he'd be able to get it sure enough, but he'd have to sell his scrawny arse to afford it. He'd done enough of that bollocks to last him six lifetimes. He'd been used and abused too much over his young life. *Fuck that for a game of fuckin' fairies*, he thought. There's a way out of this situation, a very easy way.

He took a deep breath and, 'There's this guy who lives in Kirkstall, a dealer, a big-time fuckin' dealer… Can I have a drink of water please?' His mouth was drying up. Fat Freud grunted and passed over a plastic cup of lukewarm water. 'Go on, Paul,' said Freud.

He gulped his water down like an animal, belched like a pig, and, 'Like I said, he lives in Kirkstall this guy. He gets deliveries to his flat every Thursday teatime. Without fail. Loadsa stuff, man. Thousands of Es, ounces and ounces of speed and nuff Charlie, man. Seen it wi' me own eyes I have. Fuckin' Boots the Chemist he is, man.'

Fat Freud started to shake his head. 'Yeah? Big time? Have you bought gear from him yourself?'

'Yeah, course I have…' Paul went on. 'He's a mate, kind of.'

'A mate? Don't make me laugh. If he's your mate why the fuck are you grassing him up?' Fat Freud shook his head again, as though he didn't agree with grasses.

Paul wiped the sweat from his brow and half shouted, in the quivering, smack head voice that they all have, 'I'll tell you why I'm sticking the cunt in, coz he fuckin' skanked me that's why. He sold me some fuckin' glucose powder instead of Billy. The cunt. Cost me fuckin' twenty-five quid. Hurt me teeth, man.'

Freud looked at Paul's four or five black teeth that he had left and said sarcastically, 'Ah well, twenty-five quid. He deserves it then, doesn't he? What do they call him, then? This big-time dealer. What's his name?'

Paul put his head into his clammy hands and whispered, 'Gaz.' He looked up from his hands and said in a louder voice, 'Gaz… They call him Fast Gaz.'

THURSDAY TEATIME – GAZ'S GAFF

The small radio in the kitchen was playing *Tubthumping* by Chumbawamba. I sang along as I chopped the spuds into chips.

Katie walked in and pulled a fake smile. 'You're happy, Gaz. I'm glad one of us is.' At this she started to cry into her hands.

Katie was my baby, my lady, the love of my life. Katie Farmer was her name. I'd lived here in Kirkstall with her for about three years now. She had a seven-year-old daughter, Gemma. She was a little star. I treated her just like my own. As much as I loved Katie, I hardly ever saw her, I was always out with Steve, but I lived there all the same. I first saw Katie way back in the '80s and swore to myself that she'd be mine. Well, she is now, and I treat her like a doormat. It's all gonna change though.

'Katie baby... don't cry... What's wrong?'

She simpered, 'You, Gaz... that's what's wrong. You. You treat me like a Muppet these days. You're never in. I'm sick of it. Sick to death of it all. Why can't you be normal? Thinking you're some kind of gangster. It's bollocks, Gaz. *BOLLOCKS!*'

I threw the chips into the boiling fat on top of the stove and then hugged Katie close to me.

'Listen, Katie love, I agree. You're right. I have been a twat. But that's it now. No more. Steve's locked up, he's gonna get five years or summat, and I'm giving it all up. The drugs and the DJing. I'm gonna get a proper job. I've had a good think about it, love. Trust me. You'll see.' I was, of course, chatting shit, telling her what I thought she wanted to hear. I had no real intention of giving it all up.

She pushed me away from her as the chips sizzled in the pan. 'Oh I'll see, will I?' She was being sarky now, I could tell. 'Give up the drugs, will you? There's a bloke coming in five minutes to drop you some gear off, same as every other week, isn't there? Give up the drugs, my arse.'

'Just this last time though, Katie love...' I tried to reassure her. 'He's only bringing them this last time then I'm out of it, I promise.' I gave her a huge kiss and she looked as though she believed me. And so she should, I sounded as though I really meant it. Then all holy hell broke loose.

Shouting and banging came from the flat's entrance, someone trying to break our door down. Fuck, it's the police. Armed to the teeth. Katie screamed as they exploded through the front door and pushed her out of the way. They barged into the kitchen, shouting crap, as they do.

I had the pan of chips bubbling away in my hands, and a fat cunt of a copper shouted at me, pointing his automatic at the ceiling, 'Put the pan down. *NOW!*'

I wasn't gonna ignore him, was I? He had a fuckin' gun, man. He had a gun and he thought that I was gonna burn him with chip fat. Fuck that, I don't wanna get shot. Do I? I'm sure it might sting.

I shivered a little, stood there in me boxer shorts, and gently placed the pan on the side.

'There, look…it's down.'

On putting it down they all piled into the kitchen and pinned me against the wall.

'Where's all the gear, you little cunt?' 'Where's the stuff?' 'We've got a warrant.' All that shit.

All sorts was going through my head. Where was Katie? Where was little Gemma? The Man was gonna turn up any minute and then I would be fucked. He most certainly would not be happy to arrive and see the place crawling with armed feds. I had to think. Think, Gaz man. Think.

Viva Zapata! It came to me just then and there. I struggled in the coppers' arms and twisted my head around.

'If you gimme a minute, fellas, I'll show you what it is you wanna see. You don't need to break me fuckin' flat to pieces. Or me arms.'

They were as well, emptying me cupboards, smashing stuff and knocking shit over. Bastards.

The fat one who had hold of me said, 'C'mon then, Gaz, show me the gear.'

I nodded and walked over to the little cupboard where we kept the vegetables. Inside was a bag of glucose. It was what I used for cutting shit up, but it was in a clear plastic bag. Looked just like a one pound bag of Charlie or whizz or something. The copper's face lit up like Christmas.

'Sarge…!' he shouted for his boss to come into the kitchen 'We've got the goods, Sarge. Is there anything else, Gaz?'

'Nah, man, that's it.' I bowed my head as I spoke to him.

Then they spun me around, cuffed me and gave me all the shit about my rights. They led me out to the car and Katie stood in the doorway sobbing. Little Gemma was up at the window as I was taken to the van. As they drove me up to the cop shop, I saw the Man driving towards my house in the other direction. Phew. Good timing, Gaz man. Katie'll tell him to go get himself fucked. She doesn't care if he's the "so-called Man" as she puts it.

On entering the station I got marched straight to the reception desk and was being processed when I decided to come out with it…

'Why am I being charged with drugs offences, Officer? I don't know anything about drugs. Except that they're bad of course.' I was being a smug little cunt.

The desk sergeant looked up from behind his stupid big glasses and said, 'Yeah, very funny, lad, I suppose that great bag of powder we found at your gaff is icing sugar, eh? Gonna make some fairy cakes? Ha ha.' He laughed to the other cops who were milling around the place.

'You never *found* the bag at my gaff…' I got really sarcastic now. 'I *showed* you where it was. You're not far off though when you say icing sugar. It's glucose. Pure glucose. Nothing more, sir. For me energy levels and that. I didn't know you were looking for drugs, did I? Oh, by the way, Sarge, last time I looked… possession of glucose isn't an offence. Is it?'

He glared at me, then at the police who brought me in. 'Has anyone checked that bag of powder?'

All around were muffled whispers, 'Sarge, Sarge, Sarge.'

'Chuck it here!' he shouted, and one of the young constables passed it to him. I stood looking really smug as he ripped the bag open with his key. He stuck the key in the powder, shovelled some in his mouth and… laughed his head off. '*Fucking glucose!* You mad little fucker.'

They locked me up all night anyway, just to be bastards, but when they let me go in the morning I felt like John Gotti, the

Teflon Don. I'd got one over on the feds. No charges. No fuck all.

That smell of roses is getting stronger all the time.

Right, now I'll go back home and patch it up with Katie.

CHAPTER TEN

—

TALES FROM THE DARKSIDE

Living On The Ceiling– Blancmange
(Neil Arthur and Stephen Luscombe) 1982

SUMMER 1988 – AGED 21

Apart from the terrible tragedy that was the Lockerbie Disaster, and the Bishop of Turin announcing that the famous Shroud was nothing more than a drawing of Jesus on a crappy bed sheet, a miraculous *fake*, 1988 was the Bee's Knees. The Vicar's Knickers. The Bastard's Bollocks. Get the picture yet? '88 was *the* year. Oh yes, kids, the fun starts here.

These were definitely the good times. Me, Flakey and Steve. Larging it at our house. Larging it at Fat Sally's, and larging it anywhere we could lay our beer-crazy, drug-lined hats.

It was the year that house music really exploded on to the scene, which meant only two things. Ecstasy and more ecstasy!

The Second Summer of Love they called it. They were right. Everyone loved everybody and everybody loved everyone. The boozed-up, fighting, white-shirt brigade had turned into loved-up, gurning, hugging, almost gay looking, peace-loving, ecstasy and acid fuelled dancers in baggy tee-shirts with smiley faces on the front.

We loved it, we thrived on it. I was getting more and more successful as a DJ, which meant unlimited women and unlimited drugs, in other words unlimited *fun!*

Me and Flakes lived together in my house. Steve didn't live with us but he might as well have done, he was always there. Why wouldn't he be? It was always full of women and drugs and alcohol! Everyone knew us in Leeds, we were like rock stars – free entry into all the clubs, no queuing, VIP, free cognac, free champagne and the free, free, ever so free-est of girls.

Yes, boys and girls, life was shit. Shit fuckin' hot!

We worked hard, long unsociable hours, but you know what? If you don't work, you don't get any money. And we like money.

Tonight was one of those rare occasions where I was gonna get to finish early, about twelve 'ish instead of 2am. I'd arranged for a young upcoming DJ to cover for me, so he could practise. This meant that me and Flakes could go visit some old pals of mine, Fat Cheeno and his fat brother, in Bradford, who had just opened a new club. Now, I wasn't really a fan of Bradford, "The Dark Side" as we called it, but hey, it was a well-deserved, free night out in a new place.

Steve couldn't make it tonight, he had to "go do a thing".

I played my last tune of the night, Yazz, *The Only Way Is Up*, said my goodbyes over the mic, handed over to young DJ Bernard and then we tore out of Fat Sally's the second I'd finished, even though we had quite a few girls hanging around my booth. Fuck 'em, they'll be there tomorrow. Tonight we're going for bit of fresh, Dark Side style.

We'd already taken two Es and a gram of whizz by the time we set off. We were up there with Pluto, man, and it was fucking ace! As we waited in the queue for a taxi to Bradford, Flakey looked me up and down and laughed.

'Gaz man, you're not gonna get in wi' them fuckers on yer feet.'

I had a pair of trainers on, nice ones, but trainers none the less. Now, back in 1988 you couldn't get in any nightclub, anywhere, with trainers on, even expensive ones. It had to be shoes. Or boots.

I'm buzzing my tits off in the taxi line, giggling and gurning.

'Aw, Flakes man, I'll be cushty. Fat Cheeno and his fat brother aren't gonna knock me back, are they? They're mates, man. Chill out.'

'I know, Gaz man, but what if they do though? What if they're not about when we're goin' in, and what if the bouncers are cunts? Bouncers are always cunts, man.'

I giggled even more at this, Flakey being a bouncer and all.

'Hmmm, yeah you're right, man, I don't wanna get made to look a cunt if they don't let me in. All the way to Bradford and then get knocked back by a pair of cunts, man. Nah!'

So I stuck my head out of the taxi queue and shouted down the line of people, 'Anybody wanna swap some shoes for these Adidas trainers, man? They're brand new.'

I stuck my leg out and wiggled my foot at everyone.

'I will.' This guy trotted up to me from the back of the queue. He was some sort of hippy, six foot ten and built like a brick shithouse.

Flakey laughed, I laughed, then the guy laughed.

I looked up at him and said, 'What size foot are you, big lad?'

'Size eleven.'

I laughed even more and looked at his feet. He had giant great cowboy boots on. With big wooden Cuban heels. These boots were massive, man.

'Aw man, I'm only a seven, pal, these'll never fit on your big plates.'

'Course they will. Pass 'em here.'

So I passed him one trainer. He looked at it, inspected it, sniffed it and then rubbed it on his thigh. He then took his giant boot and passed it to me. He tried sliding my trainer onto his big, swollen pig foot, squeezing, scrunching, grunting and sweating. He eventually got it on, but it looked funny, not comfy at all. I passed him the other, laughing, and he did the same routine with that one too.

'See. Told you they'd fit. Cool, mate, I'll have these, they're nice. Thanks.' He passed me the great big giant cowboy boots and fucked off down the street. Hobbling.

Me and Flakes were still laughing at him as he trundled away.

'Fuckin''ell, Flakes man, what am I supposed to do with these? Look at the size of 'em!'

He thought it was hilarious.

'They'll look nice, Gaz. Just roll some socks up in the front or summat.'

I put them on and my feet were swaying all over the shop inside them. They were huge, man. Too huge. I couldn't do anything but laugh really, even though I looked a cunt.

A lass in the queue gave me a load of tissues and I stuffed them in the boot fronts, quite snug as it goes, but they still looked a cunt.

Flakey laughed again.

'Ha ha, they look nice, Gaz man. John Wayne. You'll be cush. At least we won't get knocked back now. It'll be dark inside the club anyway. No-one'll even notice, man.'

I laughed again.

'Yeah, suppose you're right, man. Anyway, fuck all that shit, taxi's here.'

The three hours that we spent at Fat Cheeno and his fat brother's club flew by. In out shake it all about. Home time. Fuck, that was quick. That's Es and whizz for you, man.

Anyhoo, the club had been awesome. Nobody had noticed that my boots were five sizes too big and that they were high-heeled and that they looked cuntish. In fact, we danced, we drugged, we laughed and we drugged some more. We scored with a couple of tasty treats too, a rarity for Bradford, tiny little skirts and bodies from the Good Lord in Heaven.

We set off strutting down the town in order to get a taxi back to ours. These girls were up for it, man. Yes, me and Flakes are gonna take these two little buttercups to our Madhouse and they are gonna get "The Punishment". This is turning out to be a good night all round. The girls, we didn't even know their names, were walking about a hundred yards in front of us, linking arms, swaying about, giggling and shit. We were behind, chatting E'd up rubbish to each other, what we were gonna do and what we weren't gonna do to these sweethearts, when…

SCREEEECH!

Oh my Good Lord! What on earth is this all about? A white Ford Granada swerved up to the kerb where the sweethearts were, and three dudes of what can only be described as of Asian descent jumped out of the motor. Now, I've seen kidnappings on films and telly, scary stuff, but this was real, and I was off my nut! They started grabbing at the sweethearts, trying to bundle them into the car. The girls were screaming and kicking and punching and flailing, and these guys meant business, man. I shouted Flakes and ran towards the action. I almost instantly came round from my drugged-up state and went into hero mode, as did Flakey. We managed to get to them before they got pulled into the car.

The guy in the driving seat was shouting his hoppos to come on and get the fuck out of Dodge. I was dragging at the girls, as was Flakes, hoping these fellas would just fuck off. They didn't.

BANG!

I got a beauty right in the side of me napper, a right punch, man, sniper shot. I hit the floor like a sack of shit. He was just about to boot me in my lovely face when Flakes went all *Terminator* and knocked him and his mate clean out. I managed to get to my feet, reeling from the punch I'd got, stumbling around due to the great big cowboy boots, when Asian kidnapper number three flew at me like a whirling dervish. A crowd had gathered and they were pulling Flakes back as he tried to come to my rescue. One of my giant boots had come loose in the skirmish and, just as the big Asian was about to fuck me up, I pulled my giant boot clean off and *SMASH*! I swung it right under his chin, the wooden heel snapping his jaw and dropping him instantly. I was ecstatic. I jumped around like Rocky, man, his two mates knocked out by Flakey and him knocked out by a giant cowboy boot! I noticed that he had a brass knuckleduster on his fist. Fuck, man, that would have hurt! I bent down and took it from his limp hand and set off back over to Flakes and the sweethearts, when suddenly someone grabbed me from behind, choking me, telling me to calm down and shit. Fuck this, man, I'm gonna get fucked up, so I punched behind my head as hard as I could with the knuckleduster and got him slap bang in the middle of his kisser. He gave out a yelp and I turned to give him a finishing slap.

Oh no!

The sight that greeted me made me feel sick as a dog – it was a copper! I'd only gone and bust a copper's nose open. As I stood in disbelief at his exploded nose, claret everywhere, they pounced on me, three more coppers, dragged me to the deck, punched me in the temple, trussed me up like a chicken and slung me in their van. Hard. Wearing one giant cowboy boot.

Flakes got away, ran off into the night, as did the sweethearts who I ended up not doing unspeakable things to. The pigs in the back of the van, however, did their very best to make my ride to the station very uncomfortable to say the least. I was black and blue when they locked me up. My protestations to the desk sergeant fell on silent ears, he cared not one jot, his mate's nose was split in two!

I was charged with Assault on a Police Officer occasioning Actual Bodily Harm. Fuck, surely I'd get sent down for this? Two years at least, man.

When it eventually got to court my solicitor argued that as the copper got me from behind I would have had no clue as to his identity, fearing only for my life at the hands of Asian Sex Kidnappers, and God only knows what they would have done to my poor little handsome body!

Unbelievably the assault was dismissed and all I got was a fine for having the knuckleduster.

Result!

I think I'm gonna have to buy some rose-scented aftershave.

21ST AUGUST 1998 – AGED 31

When Steve got locked up, we all thought he was gonna get five years, but when it came to it the judge gave him eight years quicker than a DJ gets the girls. Whoa, not cool. And not funny either coz today it was my turn. I was finally in court for the bottle thing in Asia.

My brief said to expect at least two years. 'But you never know, Gaz, could be three, could be five.'

Fat lot of fucking good that statement does.

I'd been getting grief from Katie all morning before I set off, that I was a no-good cunt and she wasn't gonna wait for me if I got locked up and she had her own life and she wasn't gonna visit me and all that blah, blah fucking blah.

Fuck all that, I'll survive.

I'd been getting even more grief from my ex, Vicky Mancini. We'd been together five years before I met Katie, and we had three children together – Dominic nine, Jacob eight and Daisy six. Vicky was one of the girls from my little Bradford incident. Anyway, we met up again at Fat Sally's one night and then, Hey Presto three kids!

She was giving me much of the same shit as Katie had this morning. 'You're a no-good cunt, a shit father, a cunt. I'll never let you see the kids, you're a cunt.' And all that bollocks that crazy exes say and do.

Fuck all that too. I'll survive.

No option.

I turned up at court looking smooth as fuck, man, suited and booted, freshly chopped hair, boots with the pointy toes, the business. In the hope of course that the judge would look at me and say, 'Hey, Gaz man, you are *way* too cool to go to jail, now go home and don't do it again. You're looking good by the way. Love the suit.'

He didn't.

'He's a right cunt this judge, Gaz, no two ways about it, my friend.'

I'll give Mr Singh this, he's a straight talker, that's for sure. Mr Singh was my lawyer, and to all intents and purposes a good one. He'd got me, and Steve, out of many a scrape over the years. Only problem is, he talks shit! You never know what he's getting at.

'What do you mean, Mr Singh? Why's he a cunt? Who have we got?' I was flapping a bit now, man.

Mr Singh looked me directly in the eye and came straight out with it.

'You're a Catholic, right Gaz?'

'Yeah man, what's that gotta do wit' price o' prawns?'

'Say a Hail Mary or something.'

I was confused, and my arse was twitching. 'I don't get it, Mr Singh. I'm not wi' ya. What you on about, man?'

'We've got The Wombat, Gaz...' Then, somewhat disconcertingly, he placed his face in his hands. He peered up at me through his fingers and said, 'But don't worry, Gaz, the greatest defence lawyer in the land is on the case.'

'Yeah? What time does he get here?' I couldn't resist it.

He was of course referring to Judge Batty when he said we had "The Wombat", Judge Womack Batty. Although he was short-legged, hairy and muscular, much akin to the Australian marsupial of the same name, his nickname was not attributed to that, just a composite of his first and last names. He did, however, have other nicknames: Batshit, Batty Man, Batman or just plain old Batty! But The Wombat was the most used. He was crazy, man, a kind of anti-judge who always did things arse ways round – you couldn't really get a handle on which way he was gonna turn. He once sentenced a child rapist to probation, yet the following week gave a girl a month in jail for contempt of court because she wouldn't testify against her abusive boyfriend. The man was nuts. Ridiculous. He was the judge that Steve got and had given him eight years, when we all, including Mr Singh, were expecting him to get five. Fuck knows how it would go with me. Mad bastard could smile and give me community service picking up shit in the park, or he could give me a ten stretch, man, banged up with Mister Big on B-Wing!

Oh well, nowt I can do about it now, I'm going in soon.

As we waited for my turn to go into court, Mr Singh decided to boost my confidence.

'I've just come out of Court Six, Gaz, and Judge Batty was presiding. He's fucking pissed off today, I can tell you. Some cunt in there started calling him a nonce and everything when he got sentenced. He is not happy. At all. He's fucking fuming.'

'Aw cheers, Mr Singh. Thanks for that. I feel a lot better now.'

'I'm just saying, Gaz, prepare for the worst.' At that he just looked down and started shuffling his papers.

When it was eventually my turn to go in I tried to second guess the Wombat's demeanour, but he was difficult to read, just staring ahead, not at me, not at the lawyers, just ahead.

To be fair to Mr Singh, he put up a really cracking defence for me. Although I'd pleaded guilty to ABH, Actual Bodily Harm, he conveyed the truth, that I was in fact afraid for my own well-being in Asia that night. That I'd anticipated getting a good beating, so I reacted instinctively and lashed out. Pre self-defence. Retaliate first. Fight or flight. It was a them or me sort of thing.

Well done, Mr Singh.

The Wombat, however, was having none of it, man.

He stopped staring into nowhere and turned his beady eyes right at me.

'Will the defendant please stand…' I did and looked at him straight on.

'Let me be clear…' he bellowed, 'I am in no mood today for the likes of you, young man, and what's more I am in no mood for being taken for a ride, neither by yourself or by Mr So-Called Singh.'

I was twitching again, but had a little silent chuckle to myself over the Mr So-Called Singh comment. I had no clue what he meant by it.

Mr Singh looked sheepish and bowed his head like a naughty schoolboy. Aw shit, this isn't gonna be good, this batty cunt's gonna give me five years, man.

He continued, as they do, just to prolong the suspense.

'In fact, young man, in all my years as a circuit judge, I have never heard so many lies in one of my courtrooms.'

He was scaring me now, he had white shit coming out the corner of his mouth. He's a fruitcake, man, he's gonna give me a ten stretch. I can sense it.

'Quite frankly, I find your story quite preposterous.' He raised his voice, '*PREPOSTEROUS*, I say. You deliberately smashed a heavy beer bottle across another human being's head, inflicting terrible, life-changing injuries. *THIS*, I cannot let go unpunished. In fact, you have afforded me no option here today, and let me tell you, before I heard your *lies* I had considered leniency, but *no* not now. There is no alternative to a custodial sentence for *liars* such as you. Liars go to jail. I hereby sentence you to...' He paused, on purpose, as they do, for what seemed like eighteen long minutes, and then, 'Twelve...' Fuck, another long pause. This cunt's got liar issues and he's gonna give me twelve years. '...months in prison. Take him down.'

Fuck me! Twelve months? I thought he was gonna throw away the bastarding key, the way he was ranting and raving. Twelve months? That means I'll only do six. Result, man.

Mr So-Called Singh had been giving me all sorts of shitty scenarios, but not the one where I only serve six months. I love Mr Singh. Just five minutes ago this batshit crazy Judge Wombat was creating as though I was the Son of Satan. Made me think I was gonna get lifed off!

Result! Result! Result!

Not exactly the smell of roses that I'd become accustomed to over the years.

But it was pretty fuckin' close.

—

CHAPTER ELEVEN

JOE COCAINE

No One Is Innocent–
The Sex Pistols and Ronnie Biggs
(Paul Cook, Steve Jones, R Biggs)

22ND AUGUST 1998 – THE NEXT DAY

Fyodor Dostoyevsky, the famed Russian author of *Crime and Punishment,* reckoned that you could tell the state of the society you lived in by entering into its prisons. He also said that people tended to get carried away with their little selves and make mistakes, but that men must have indulgences, so therefore those mistakes were merely evidence of over enthusiasm.

Bless him.

I'd just spent my first night behind bars. They took me straight to Leeds jail. The Big House. A nasty looking, imposing, stone Victorian monstrosity, if ever you saw one. Just like you

see on the films and telly, rows and rows of cells, and landings
with suicide nets between them.

To be fair, my first night had gone without incident – booked in,
had some tea, went to bed. No biggy. The main problem with this
gaff was that I was locked up twenty-three hours a day. I was only
due to be there a couple of weeks till I got shipped out. Boredom
soon sets in, man, and I never get bored. I have a saying that only
boring people get bored, but fuck that, man, I was bored in there.

You could use the gym for an hour on a morning if you
wanted, so I thought I'd give that a go to relieve some snail-pace
time.

I soon changed my mind when I got there and saw that
Hercules was the gym orderly. I knew Hercules from outside,
he was well known. He was big and Greek and muscly, with
a neck bigger than my chest. He'd remind you of Arnold
Schwarzenegger to look at, but meaner. He was also a persistent
violent rapist. Of women *and* men! He was well known on the
inside for having some sort of deal with the screws, whereby they
brought the more vulnerable young men to his pad and then he
did whatever the Hell it was he did to the poor cunts once he
got them in his cell. His favourite phrase to the screws, whilst
chucking the poor, destroyed young 'un from his cell, was, 'Pass
me another, this one's ripped!' Not a nice fella. To say the least.

I walked into the gym and he was lifting weights and
sweating and grunting and then he copped me. 'Hey, Gazzy boy.
C'mere, man. What you doing here?'

'I just got here, Herc man, thought I'd give gym a try, y'know
build me sen up a bit.'

He licked his lips. 'I'll look after you, Gaz. I'll build you up.
Mmmm yes.'

Fucking hell, man, I don't want this cunt "looking after me".
It'd just end in ruptures and torn flesh. In places you don't want
ruptures and torn flesh!

'I'm just having a look today, pal...' I twitchingly answered, 'but I'll be back down tomorrow, Hercules man.'

At that, I did an about turn and hotfooted it out of there. I never went back either. In fact, I never set foot in any gym ever again, anywhere, inside the nick or outside. Ever. Just in case.

I like being slim anyway. And unraped.

My time in Leeds jail was uneventful. I was only there three weeks and all I'd done was eat, read, walked round an exercise yard full of cunts who thought they were arch criminals, and listened to shit from the five different smack head pad mates I got during that time.

Sea View Camp, however, was a different kettle of bollocks altogether. That was the name of the prison I got shipped out to. It was miles from Leeds, down on the Norfolk coast, man, but I didn't want any visitors so I didn't care. Visitors just upset you, man. They'll still be there when you get out, so why cause yourself heartache?

The Camp, as it was known, was a Category D prison, an open prison, minimum security for low-risk offenders, short-term prisoners and guys coming to the end of really long sentences, lifers and shit.

You can't fault this place, man, it's not even like a nick. It's a series of cabins for the inmates to stay in, a former army base. Just two guys to each room, no overcrowding, no locks on the pad doors, windows without bars, curtains, no toilet in the room, no fences, no walls, just a little two-foot hedgerow, and you could see the sea at the bottom of the sports pitch. The no fences thing was all done on trust – they trust you not to try to abscond and you trust them for trusting you. This, of course, didn't stop guys from fucking off on a weekend coz they thought their wife or bird was gonna go to a pub or summat. Or look at another man. Or worse. Pointless really. They'd always get caught and then get put back in a top security place. No Cat D ever again. I couldn't weigh it up. The shit they get into over women.

After your job, you had to either work or be in education, no skiving like in Leeds, but you had the run of the place, you could go from pad to pad chatting to your pals, play pool, watch telly, play darts, even though the darts were Velcro, for obvious reasons, play cards, phone your mam, walk round the grounds and take in the sea air, whatever. It was cush, man. I could see why some people love prison.

THREE MONTHS LATER — NOVEMBER 1998

When I first got here, I thought I was gonna be like a fish out of water, but not so, I settled in really well. Too well for my liking, I quite enjoyed it, man! Not to the point where I wanted to stay for good, or ever come back for that matter, nah, fuck that shit, but I did stay positive, and certainly made the most of it.

I'd spent my first week in The Camp working on "The Cleaners". This is just as it sounds, cleaning. Cleaning corridors, cleaning communal areas, cleaning bogs, cleaning walls, just fucking cleaning, man. It was horrible. Not because it was cleaning, no man, that didn't bother me; after all, shit needs to be clean, doesn't it? No, man, it was the boredom of it. You only worked for two hours on The Cleaners, two hours on a morning, and then the rest of the day to do whatever you wanted.

A lot of the guys loved it, saw it as a cushy number, lazy cunts. Not me, man, all it did was drag out your time. You'd start at 9am after your breakfast and work till 11am. Then what? Lie on your bed looking at the clock and the calendar? Read? Only so much reading you can do. Wank yourself stupid? Well, that's not bad until some cunt comes wandering into your pad to borrow some bog roll or summat and you're on the vinegar stroke, chatting porno shit to yourself! Got embarrassing after a while. I even tried a "stranglewank" once, you know, the auto-erotic asphyxiation shit that rock stars and politicians always die of. With a tangerine in their mouth. Didn't like that shit, man, it was scary. Thought I was gonna die myself. Imagine my mother hearing that bollocks! That I'd died hanging from a cell door with my dick in my hand and a fucking little orange in my mouth!

You could go to the shower block to knock one out but that was some form of nasty degenerate shit in itself. You see, the showers weren't like you see in the films, with all the guys in one big shower room, nah man, there were six cubicles, for three hundred prisoners! The cubicles, to be fair, had a curtain, but there was always a line of fuckers outside waiting for their turn. They knew what you were up to so it was still embarrassing, curtain or not. But worst of all, the cubicles had the plastic shower trays that you stood in, with a plug hole that, more often than not, was blocked. So these trays would fill with water and body scum, but more horrifyingly, when you shot your load it also went into the blocked tray. Imagine, you're the twenty-third to get in the shower today, your feet are swimming in twenty-three different specimens of spunk, man. Double nasty. Everyone got some sort of fungal foot disease after using those showers, man.

Nah. Fuck that, cleaning duty wasn't for me. I wanted a job where I could work all day to pass my time quickly, and where I wouldn't have to resort to wanking in the spunk shower all day out of sheer boredom.

I fell lucky. I got a job in the kitchens, pot wash, 7am till 6pm. Perfect. Wash dishes and pans and shit all bleedin' day long. It went really fast each day and I got to chat bollocks with the guys. It was a cushy number for me coz not only did it pass the time and give me some well needed conversation, it made me *money*!

Now listen up, I'm not talking about the wages, I only got five pound fifty wages for working eleven hours a day six days a week. No real chance of becoming Rockefeller with that, are you?

No, man, I became a *food dealer!*

Anything I could scam from the kitchen I would, but my main deal was coffee and cheese. The guys would go mad for it. I'd nick it and they'd come to my pad and pay me top dollar for it. I had jars and jars of coffee round my pad, and giant industrial slabs of cheese under my bed.

I wasn't exactly Joe Cocaine, but it got me by, and it gave me a buzz.

All the lads in the shovel were mostly okay, there were a few cunts, but you get them anywhere, not just jail. But the blokes in here, in the main, just wanted to get their heads down and do their time. Nobody went round bumming and bashing, leave that to the young offenders and maximum security gaffs. This place was nice and easy, sell some cheesy.

My pad mate was a top lad, Shuffles was his name, on account that he walked funny, bit of a leg dragger, a shuffler. Despite his inability to walk in straight lines, we had a little scam going from our cell that worked just fine for us both. Because I was earning a few quid with my kitchen dealing, I was also able to be "The Pop Man". This involved selling vodka to the other guys. There were plenty of fellas selling drugs in there, but fuck that, too risky, man. A bit of booze is no great shakes though.

It went like this. Get Shuffles to go round the pads taking orders, vodka only, it's easier to conceal in your orange juice or wherever. Then he'd come to me with usually about a ten bottle order, I'd give him the money, and then he'd just walk over the field and into town to the off licence. Bold as fuckin brass! It usually took him an hour or so coz he was a shuffler, but he got the job done. Bless his filthy, never been changed or washed, cotton socks.

He'd come back with his backpack full of vodka, that had cost me seven fifty a bottle, and then we'd sell it for twenty quid. I always paid for a bottle for him, that was his cut for doing all the dirty work, it's all he wanted. Everyone's happy, everyone's a winner.

I got to meet lots of different types of fellas in The Camp, some more memorable than others. I'd often write about them in my letters to Steve. Everyone in prison writes more or less the same shite in every letter: I love you, I hate you, let's get married, I'm gonna change, I'll never do it again, honest, and blurgh, blurgh, blurgh. Not me, I just wrote about the people I met, sometimes over exaggerating to make it more interesting, sometimes not having to at all. Steve's letters to me, however, were very short and to the point, to say the very least. Always six words long. Always.

LETTER TO STEVE

Hey up, Stevie Baby,

How's it going up there, man? Hope all is well and you've not got yourself into too much grief, pal. Anyway, bud, I enjoyed your last letter, all six words of it. Since then I've met quite a few new mates. You already know about Shuffles, he's a good lad, he gets out in a couple of week, but I'll be okay, man, I'll get a new pad mate and just carry on doing me time, pal. Same old same old.

I don't write to Katie, man, can't be arsed. I only write to you and me mam, odd letter to the kids, but they're only young so don't really understand.

Anyway, let me tell you about some more of the gadges I've met.

There's Slinky. He's alright I suppose, he looks a right cunt though, bubble perm like an '80s Scouser. Always got a dirty face an' all. He's doing an eighteen monther for nicking an old bloke's watch. Sounds a bit harsh till you realise that Slinky had gone to help the poor old cunt who'd just been run over by a Renault Clio at a junction, he spotted the Gucci watch on the old fucker's wrist and, instead of helping the poor twitching cunt, took his fucking watch off and hit the wind, man. Bit dirty I suppose, but hey ho! I asked him if the old fella lived and he just shrugged his shoulders, man. He buys cheese off me every day!

Then there's Bad Luck Bill. He's coming to the end of an eight stretch for manslaughter. He was originally doing two years for burglary, which he denied. Anyway, he got into a fight in Durham nick and killed a bloke. The bad shit is though, man, that his appeal for the burglary came through in his favour, with DNA or summat, he wasn't guilty after all, shouldn't have even been inside in the first place, man, but the poor cunt's still got to do the eight year for the manslaughter! Ha ha, I know it's not funny really, but it kind of is. He buys cheese and coffee off me now and again.

There's Paddy. He's a Paddy, from Dublin like my dad, he's small and scrawny with untold amounts of acne and tells everyone wild stories, bit like me, man! He keeps trying to convince everyone that St Brendan discovered America a thousand years before Christopher Columbus. And that he went in a little rowing boat from Galway. And wrote about Red Indians in his diaries! Who knows, man, could be true, but you know what I say, never believe an Irishman! Ha ha.

There's a guy who's Russian, Blood Piss is his nickname. Don't know much about him, no-one does. He just comes to my pad, buys some vodka, listens to all the bullshit on offer and then fucks off. None of us even know what he's in for. He doesn't speak a stroke of English, man; only one word I ever hear him say is 'BEETROOT!' when he comes to the canteen for dinner. All he eats, man, fucking beetroot. Makes his piss red by all accounts. I haven't had a look, Stevie Boy. And don't fucking intend to either! Ha ha.

There are four pikeys that come round for vodka all the time. They're alright, no bother, can hardly understand 'em though, they just laugh and slap their big pikey hands on the table and on each other's backs and talk gibberish to each other. All four of 'em are called Johnny Boy! All of 'em, man. Mad.

Frankie Fat Knackers is funny, Stevie man, you'd piss yer sen if you saw him, he's got Bollocks as Big as a Bread Bin! He's got a party piece that he does when he comes round. He likes to get his giant nads out and then shows you that he can't even fit *one* of 'em in the top of a pint glass. It's gross, but funny. He does it all the time when he's on the out too, in pubs and shit, even in the bingo hall, man! All the old dears love it apparently. He even got a job on the outside to accommodate his big spuds, lying on his back on a little trolley underneath cars, in a garage or summat. Each one is like a fucking Big Red Grapefruit. But heavier! The weight of his bollocks has even dragged his cock inside his body, leaving a great big, wet, gaping, doughnut hole where his cock should be. Looks awful, Stevie man. If he had a wife who loved him and doted on him, which he hasn't, even she'd be sick, man. He doesn't buy fuck all off me, just comes round to get his plums out.

Then there's Jack the Cat. He's called that because he's died eight times! Yeah, man, keeps overdosing and dying for a minute or summat then coming back alive.

Only one life left for that cunt, man. He's only doing three month, shoplifter, junkie, you know the score, man. He seems okay but we all watch our shit when he's about. You know what they're like, man, them coat-feeling cunts, especially if they know they've only got one life left! Ha ha.

Then there's Bang Bang, another smack head, doing nine months for robbing shops with one of them toy guns that the red cloth thing comes out the end with *BANG* written on it! Daft cunt.

There's Chinese Sammy, who's English but looks Chinese, funny yoks and that, and his mate English Jimmy, who *is* Chinese but tells everyone he's English coz he's from Hong Kong. Funny pair them two. I think they're at it to be fair, if you get what I mean. They asked me if I could get them some beef mince! Ha ha.

Hope I'm not boring you yet, Stevie baby. I know you're doing a big bitch sentence so I like to keep you occupied, me old mate, not like the six word letters you send me! Nah, only kidding, pal, I know you can't write very well. Ha ha.

Anyway, there's a kid called Hypo, always in and out, man, three month here, five month there, all that shit, burglar and shoplifter. Anyway he's a right hypochondriac, man, always in the clinic for summat or other. When he was on the out his doctor got that sick of him coming everyday with whatever bullshit ailment he said he had, that he had him admitted to hospital and got 'em to take his appendix out to shut him the fuck up. So he'd have a scar to show off. Nutter, man! Now he goes on about his throat and his teeth and his bones are loose and all manner of shit, man. He gets vodka off me though, so I like him. Loose bones or not!

Then there's Jacko, a little Brummie, always fighting with cunts and getting locked up. Anyhoo, last time he was in, he got in a rumble in the kitchens and some cunt stuck his hand in a pan of boiling stew, took all his skin off, came off like a glove, man. One of his hands is fucked now, man. One ungloved hand, hence Jacko! He's alright an' all, chats shit, but he's alright. He can't sing like Jacko though.

A good lad that's been looking after me, making sure I don't get any shit or owt, is Frosty, Gideon Frost, big black fella. I sort him out with vodka, he makes sure no cunt wants to rip me off. He gets out around same time as me so it's good good good, man. No cunt messes with him, Stevie boy, and that in turn means no cunt messes with me! Result! Big Black Rupert tried to start with me the other night in the telly room. All I did was fart, man. It was ripe enough, I'll give it that, but not to the extent that Mad Black Rupert should start shouting, 'It's not human, man, I'll keeeel you,' and all that shit, so Frosty went up to him, whispered summat in his lug, and he shut the fuck up and toddled off, Bumbo clarting under his breath. Ha ha haaa!

There's one kid, Junkie he's called, and he's *not* a junkie, never touched drugs, doing twelve month for fraud. Nah, man, they call him Junkie coz his name's Tom Major and when he was at school in the '80s the teacher would do the class register on a morning and when he got to him he'd say his surname first then his first name, Major? Tom? then all his class would shout out the lyrics to *Ashes to Ashes* and Major Tom being a Junkie! Every morning! Poor cunt. Even the teacher sang it.

Then there's Puddy. Steve man, he's a weird one, not really scary, but a proper weirdo. He's coming to the end of an eleven-year stretch, man. He won't tell us what he did, just keeps saying that he was set up by them bitches, but I had it on good authority, one of the better screws, that Puddy was a kidnapper. Not in the "we want a ransom" sense, nah man, apparently all he did was kidnap pregnant women, tie 'em up for half an hour, milk 'em, then let 'em go. Yep, you read that right, Steve man, *fucking milked* them! Ha ha ha ha. Eleven year though? Bit harsh. Ha ha.

There's a nice old fella that comes round for a vodka, about seventy he is, man, Christmas Pete he's called, just coming to the end of a ten stretch. Seems like butter wouldn't melt in his snaffle, but he's a cool customer, man. A few Christmases ago he was sat in a bar in Hull, where he's from, minding his business, when three young out of town pricks started tormenting him, calling him a fossil and chucking peanuts at him and shit, thinking they were ten men, with a sixty odd year old bloke. Anyway, as it so happens, Christmas Pete is well respected round that way and there were some local young hard nuts in the bar playing pool.

Watching.

Now, Pete noticed that the locals had seen what was going on, so he gave the pricktards an ultimatum. He said, not shouting, just calmly, 'Right, children, I'm gonna give you two choices here. If you look over there…' he pointed at the local nut jobs, 'they're gonna beat you till you're all paralysed, with pool cues, *PA-RA-LYSED!*' He said you could hear them all gulp, and the fear in their "not so fucking hard now, are they" eyes was clearly visible by the well of tears coming in to them, when one of them piped up, trembling like a baby lamb, 'What's the other choice, Mister?'

'Ha, or, young man, *I'M* gonna beat you, with a pool cue, till you are paralysed, all of you.' And at that point he raised his voice, *'PARA-FUCKING-PLEGIC!'* then flew at them like an animal. The locals flew at them too, and they and Christmas Pete did indeed give them the hiding of their sorry, soon to be not a very good quality of life, life.

Christmas Pete was true to his word. Each of them ended up either para or quadriplegic, man.

Moral of that story, Stevie man, *never* chuck salted peanuts at some old gimmer sat at the bar, or it could well be Stephen Fucking Hawking time!

Nice bloke though. Buys cheese, coffee *and* vodka!

The last fella I'm gonna tell you about, Stevie, is a real horror show, man. He's coming to the end of a life sentence, mate, the big bitch. He's got two years left to do in here. He's already done twenty-two years, man, all over the gaff, Wakefield, Broadmoor, now here! He's not all there, man, but keeps coming round asking for cheese and shit, and nobody dares to say no to him.

Angry Leonard's his name. He doesn't seem really angry now to be fair, and he's only a little fella, about fifty, bit of a Bobby Charlton comb over that looks a cunt, but before he got sent down, man, he was one angry, mean-spirited, horrible little cunt.

Apparently, and it was in all the papers, he was bang at it all the time on gin and throttle, pissed out of his tits and whizzing his brains off. Anyway, he went out of his tiny mind one day and killed his pregnant girlfriend, with a screwdriver, stabbed her up bad style, man, all over her head, in their own living room. Then, when she was dead on the carpet, he went in his kitchen, got a Budweiser out the fridge and sat and drank it, staring at her mangled body. After he finished the beer, he broke the bottle over her dead head and cut her belly open with it, pulled the baby out of her guts and killed it an' all! He pulled its eyes out with the broken bottle then went in his garden and tied the dead baby to a breezeblock, walked fifty yards down the street to his girlfriend's mam's house and threw it through her living room window while she was sat watching Sale of the fucking Century man. He then sat on her garden wall, lit a cig and waited for the law to come, mumbling and crying to himself. That's nuts that, Stevie man. He's nuts, man. That Angry Leonard definitely has Dreadful Demons Dancing in his deranged head! And now they think he's okay to come here, with us normal cunts, man, even Puddy the Tit Milker seems normal next to this crazy cunt.

Anyway, I give him cheese for fuck all, daren't ask him to pay! Ha ha. Even Frosty's wary of him and he's a right hard cunt.

Right, man, hope you've enjoyed my letter, my old pal, hope you write back soon, bud. Try make it a bit longer this time, matey, keep out of trouble and I'll see you when I see you, fella me lad. I'll write next week, man. Bye for now.

Your Pal, Gaz x

And that was my letter to Unsolved Steve, six pages long. I had fun writing it, passes mine and his time, and I'm sure he shows them to his pals in there and has a laugh. I just wish his letters were longer. I like a good read.

Steve's letter came five days later. As always I got a bit giddy, as when receiving any letter. I opened it gently and unfolded the letter. Didn't take me long to read it though, same six fucking words as usual, it read: "Gaz man, you're full of shit."

23RD DECEMBER 1998

Alexander Hamilton, one of the founding fathers of the USA said, "The fondness for power is implanted in most men, and it is natural to abuse it when acquired."

I've never had a problem with authority, as such, just those who abuse the position. They're cunts.

Now, most of the screws in The Camp were cush, fifty and sixty somethings coming to the end of their service, getting ready to retire, not wanting any hassle and just getting on with their time, just like us I suppose. It made for a nice steady atmosphere the majority of the time. However, there were a couple of younger screws, early twenties, just starting out and trying to make a name for themselves. Like cunts.

They reminded me a little of one of my teachers at high school, Mr McFadden. He was only young, and he was a fucking bully, man. He was my Latin teacher and he once threw his big size ten clodhopper at my Swede for staring him out. I shoulda looked away when he told me to, but me being me, never backing down and never shutting the fuck up when I really ought to, carried on with the stare out. Bosh, leather brogue up side my head. Ah well, shit happens sometimes.

One such officer was Officer Snellgrove. He was only twenty-three years old, and he was a right bandy legged, knock-kneed, pincey toed, humpty backed, long-necked, big-nosed, cross-eyed bastard. And because he had such ridiculous features, he took it upon himself to be the biggest bully of all, coz he looked a cunt. The cunt.

Anyway, man, it was a normal day at The Camp and I'd just finished washing all the breakfast pots in the kitchens, getting all the black, ingrained shit off the pans and restoring them back to their original stainless steel colour, no mean feat I can tell you. I was fucking knackered, man, and in no mood for any cunt, least of all a mardy arse bastard young kid of a cunt of a screw.

I had a thirty minute break before I had to get back to graft to help prepare lunch, so went outside the block for a smoke. I chatted bollocks with some of the lads and the kitchen screw, Miss Carter. She was alright, a good one. If you were nice, she was nice, if you were a bastard, she was a bastard. Like I say, a good one.

After my fag, I needed to go for a piss, so off I toddled, down the corridor to the bogs. When I walked in there was Office Snellgrove checking his funny hair in the mirror, no-one else, just him. I didn't say anything to him, just acknowledged him with a nod, and he said nothing either, just looked me up and down. Like a cunt.

I got my big cock out, that I'm very proud of by the way, and proceeded to jet my piss against the porcelain. Aaaaah, the feeling was immense, I'd been saving it all morning, it lasted nearly a minute, man. Then, as I was tucking it back away, I heard from behind me:

'You.' It was Officer Cunt Face.

'Me?' I asked, knowing full well he meant me as there was no other fucker about.

'Yeah, you. Clean that shit up.' He pointed to a slob of human shit on the wall near the bottom of the urinal. How it got there I've no fucking clue, you never know with some of these dirty bastards in here.

I turned my head to take a look, grimaced at it and said:

'Boss, you want *me* to clean that human shit off the wall? I'm kitchen staff, boss, not cleaners.'

He gave a cuntish little fuck face smile and replied:

'I don't give a toss what you are, inmate, you'll do as you're told. I give an order, you do it, now clean that shit up.' Still smiling, the fucker.

'But, boss, I've got my kitchen whites on, I've gotta go back in and help prepare the mutton stew. Can't be cleaning human shit up in me whites, boss. Can I?' He can fuck right off, I'm not doing it, I don't give a monkey's fuck, man.

He stopped smiling and came square up in my face, about an inch from my nose.

'Listen, you little thieving fucker, or whatever the fuck you're in for, I'm the fucking boss and you'll do as I fucking tell you, or you'll go on governor's report. Now fucking *clean… it… up… now!'*

I stared into his crossed eye, as I had all those years ago with Mr Mc-Fuckin'-Big-Shoe-Fadden, thought about the governor's report for a moment, and then:

'Fuck that, *you* fuckin' clean it up.' And I marched out, quick time.

I thought he was gonna follow me and give me a dig or summat, but no, not a sign of him, didn't see him at all for the rest of that day. I'm glad too, coz he's a cunt.

I had a laugh with Shuffles and the lads that night in my pad, telling them all about my bog incident. The lads all said that I should have just done it, cleaned it up. Fuck that, it was the way he asked. Fuck him.

The next morning was like every other morning, up with the sparrows, get to the kitchens and prepare breakfast for everyone. We, the kitchen staff, would serve all the other prisoners, then get ours and go out and join them.

Whilst eating brekkie, there was a morning ritual that consisted of one of the officers shouting names over the tannoy. If your name was shouted out it meant you'd broke some rule or done some shit and you had to go to the governor's office. It was a funny ritual. The screw would shout the name, the guilty party would stand up and everyone in the dining hall would clap and cheer or shout bollocks at them, then they'd trot over to the screw on the watch to be taken to Mr Bray's office, the governor.

This morning was no exception, apart from the fact that I was expecting my name to come up from the bog thing. You never know, I might be lucky.

The first name came over the speaker, 'Warburton, Andrew,' and up he stood, poor Andy, everyone clapping and cheering.

I thought my name was coming next, but:

'Major, Tom.' Well, this just resulted in everyone in the room singing in unison the words to *Ashes to Ashes* and being a Junkie. Even the screws were singing it, and poor Tom went bright red and scuttled off on report.

Then silence over the tannoy, more silence, then everyone started back chattering to each other and talking shite about what they thought Andy and Tom had done and what punishment they'd get. I was just glad that my name hadn't come out. I felt all warm and content inside, when…

My fucking name got called bastard out.

Everyone clapped, everyone cheered, I acted not bothered, which I was, but acted cool nonetheless and strutted over to the duty screw to be taken to the Big Boss Man. Cunts.

Even though I got called last I was taken into Mr Bray's office first whilst the others stood outside against the radiator.

The duty screw took me in and, as I got inside, Mr Bray the governor was sat behind his giant walnut desk, looking down at some papers, tapping a fountain pen, and Officer SnellCunt was stood alongside him, smirking.

I was placed about six foot away from his desk when he looked up over his specs and said:

'Right, young man, you are here this morning on a charge of insubordination, refusing to carry out a direct order from an officer, namely Officer Snellgrove. What do you have to say for yourself?'

I paused, and then stared directly at Mr Bray.

'Sir, there's nothing *to* say really. Officer Snellgrove was being unreasonable. He wanted me to clean up fresh, human faeces whilst I was wearing my kitchen whites, sir. Wouldn't have been very healthy for the kitchen, sir, all sorts of germs, sir, E. coli and what not.'

He kinda glared at Officer Cuntgrove and said:

'Is this true, Officer Snellgrove?'

Officer Cross-eyed Cunt looked like a naughty schoolboy and leaned into Mr Bray and whispered something in his lug. Mr Bray then whispered something into Snellie's lug. They both nodded to each other and then turned to me.

'Here's how it is, young man...' said Mr Bray sternly, like a schoolteacher, 'if you apologise to Officer Snellgrove, then we shall say no more about the matter and you can go back to your duties. How does that sound? Is that fair?'

I could tell by this that Mr Bray wasn't happy with Cunty Face, that he knew he had been harsh, so:

'Apologise for what, sir? He was being unreasonable, as I'm sure you'll agree.' I tried to get him more on my side than he already was.

'That's as maybe, young man, however Officer Snellgrove *is* an officer and you disobeyed a direct order, so make your apology and let me get back to doing what it is that I do, which is, I can assure you, something far more important than this.'

'I didn't do anything to apologise for, sir, so no, with respect, I won't apologise, sir.'

He had a little twitch in the corner of his right eye now, and Snells was looking mighty uncomfortable too. Well good, he shouldn't be a bully.

He gave me one last opportunity.

'Listen to me, young man, you are not doing yourself any favours here. Right or wrong, you disobeyed an officer, so apologise, now, or I'll have no alternative but to add extra time on to your sentence.'

I was seething inside at this comment. Extra time? For not apologising to a fucking bully, well fuck that, I'm not saying sorry, not to that cunt. What's the worst he can give me? Two days? Three days? Fuck it, I'll take my chance.

'Again, Mr Bray, sir, with respect, I'm not gonna apologise when I didn't do owt wrong. Sir. And that's that. Do what you want.' I felt more than just a little smug saying this, especially as I could see CuntSnell squirming in his shoes.

'Very well, then.' Mr Bray looked back down at his papers and began to write something, and without looking back up he said, 'You have given me no choice. I, on the other hand, *did* give you a choice, which you decided to ignore. Life is all about choices, young man. You'll learn. Twenty-eight days added onto your sentence, starting from now. Take him out.'

Fucking cunt, man, an extra month? An extra fucking *month*? Well, fuck 'em, I'll do my month, I'll only have to do half anyway, still two weeks though, bit harsh, but hey! I stood my fucking ground, man. I won't be bullied.

I thought Officer Snellgrove was gonna be a right cunt after that, even more than he already was, but I was wrong. I wouldn't say he was nice, no, no, no, not by any stretch of even the most vivid imagination, but he did leave me alone, didn't try and fire down retribution or any other such bollocks, he just kept completely out of my way, as did I his.

The cunt.

TWO WEEKS LATER – JANUARY 1999

Christmas had been and gone. It wasn't much, as you'd expect really, being in prison and all. Some of the lads had absconded, and then got caught again, sent to more secure nicks, the mad twats. I could half understand them, missing their wives and shit, but running off, man, nah. Me and Shuffles and the lads that hadn't ran off made the best of it, got loads of alcohol, got fucked up, and mainly just chatted bollocks! Same old same old.

Anyway, now it's January, it's snowy, I'll be out in about seven weeks, which is good, but what isn't good is that my pal Shuffles is getting out tomorrow morning. It is good that he's getting out, course it is, but I'll miss him, man, it's shit having to get a new pad mate. What if he's a complete tool? What if he's a screamer or a nutcase or, worse, a screaming sex case?! I wish my good friend Shuffles was staying, but hey ho.

That night we were lying in our beds, chatting away. We only had the little lamp on as the moon was real bright, shining through the snow-speckled window, and the radio was on quietly in the corner, some saxophone jazz that they always seem to play at night-time.

I'd never asked Shuffles about his funny legs, why he walked like he did, just never crossed my mind, up to now.

'Shuffs man.' I laid on my side and put my head on my hand, elbow on the bed.

'Yeah, Gaz man, what's up?' He looked across from his bed, inquisitively.

'You've never told me what happen to your pins, man. Were you in an accident or summat?' He looked a little shy and apprehensive at me, so I said, 'Aw mate, you don't have to tell me, I was just trying to pass the time, pal, no worries, forget I ever said owt, Shuffs man. Sorry for asking, buddy.'

I felt bad for asking, but then he gave a little sigh and decided to tell me his tale.

'It's okay, Gaz pal, I've just never told anyone before that's all, but you're the best friend I've ever had in my life, you look after me, you and Frosty and the boys, I'll miss you all, you're my family, Gaz man. I don't even wanna get out tomorrow, I wanna stay here with you lot, my family. People laugh at me out there, fuck, *you'd* laugh at me out there. I love it here, I don't wanna go home, man.'

I listened intently as I saw his eyes well up with water and he continued his story:

'You see, Gaz, I have no family on the outside, no-one. My dad was an alky who beat on my mam whenever he could, and he left her the day after I was born, saying he couldn't handle having a kid. Never came back either. My mam always blamed me for him leaving, even though she was better off without him, but she'd shout at me and say horrible shit to me like she wished she'd had an abortion and all that crap. Bitch. I was disabled from birth, Gaz man, couldn't walk, no use in my legs. I was never placed on the floor, ever, always in a pram, or a cot, or on a sofa or summat. Then, as I got older, a wheelchair. She kept me off school, taught me at home, fat lot of fuckin' good that did, the thick bitch. I lived with her, just me and her and nobody from the outside world ever coming to see us or anything, just her wheeling me around the park or to the off licence for fucking cider. Then, Gaz man, one day when I was twenty-two, I'm thirty now by the way, she died. I found her, dead on the living room carpet. She'd drunk two bottles of vodka and taken a load of temazzies. Blue she was. It was awful. It was awful, but I was glad, can you believe that, Gaz man? I was glad she was dead. I called an ambulance, they came, they took her, and that was that, I was alone, just me, nobody else. I drank a bottle of Smirnoff and fucked off asleep. Didn't even go to her funeral, man. You know why?'

'No man, why?' I had a tear in my eye at this point.

'I'll tell you why, Gaz man, coz the day after they took her away, a social worker came to see me, to sort me out with my disability care and shit, and guess what... I had tests at the hospital and shit, and it worked out that I wasn't even disabled, man. I wasn't even *fucking* disabled!'

He was getting tetchy with himself now, angry and red in the face.

'What do you mean, pal? You weren't disabled? How do you mean, man?'

He had a sad but mean looking scowl on his face as he continued.

'She made me like this. I had fuck all wrong with me, Gaz, *fuck all!* From being a little baby she'd kept me from learning to walk, kept me in a pram, kept me on the sofa, kept me in bed, carried me, whatever, whatever she could to stop me from learning to walk. She made me think I couldn't walk, she told me I was disabled, so I believed her, she was my mother, man, so I *fuckin' believed her.* All those fucking years, man, I could've walked, could have had a normal life, man. The other kids calling me Spaz and Flid, and she kept me a gimp, all so she could get extra money for me, for the disabled kid. *Extra fuckin' money!*'

He was sobbing now. I sat up and went over to his bed and put my arm round him, tried to comfort him.

'Shuffs man, fuckin' hell, that's some story, my poor pal, you've had it rough, bud. You're okay now though, mate, aren't you?'

'S'pose so, Gaz man, I can kinda walk now at least. My legs are skinny and fucked, but fuck all that shit, Gaz, I just wish I didn't have to leave tomorrow, man. I'll miss you all.' And he put his arms round me and sobbed uncontrollably. 'I've never even been to a nightclub, Gaz man, a disco, a dance, nowt, never.'

Still with my arms around him I tried to give some words of comfort, 'Shuffs man, when I get out I'll come meet you, pal. We'll go dancing. We'll set the town on fire. It'll be like *Saturday Night Fever*, mate.'

'Ha...!' He pulled away and looked at me with a frown. 'You won't, Gaz man, you'll forget about me when you get out. Everyone does. It's alright for you, bud, you're cool and good-looking. I'm not, I'm a freak, man. I won't fit in properly in them places. You won't meet me. I wouldn't want to meet me either if I was you. So do me a favour, don't say you will. Be a pal and don't lie.' At that he took a breath, a deep sad sigh and climbed into his bed.

He was right though, as bad as it makes me feel, I probably wouldn't have met him, and yeah, he wouldn't fit in. The fuckers I knew would have laughed at him. And at me for bringing him.

The next morning, he was gone before I woke up. The screws had come really early to take him for release. I thought about his sad story the night before and another tear came to my eye. Poor Shuffles, I hope he's gonna be okay.

He wasn't.

I learned two days later from Miss Carter, the kitchen screw, that Shuffles, real name Christopher Neville, had got back to his shitty flat on the night he was released, put on some nice clothes, did his hair, put on some nightclub music, drank two bottles of shit vodka, then ate a packet of temazepam.

And he died.

When they found him, lying on his sofa, he had his arms crossed on his chest.

In one of his hands was a tiny photograph.

It was his mother.

CHAPTER TWELVE

—

PARTY OVER?

Being Boring–
The Pet Shop Boys (Chris Lowe, Neil Tennant)

MARCH 5TH 1999 — AGED 32

I came around from a deep slumber not knowing where on God's green earth I was, I rubbed my yoks and shifted upwards in my seat. I'd fallen asleep on the train, man. I'd been asleep for over an hour. Not surprising really. I'd been up since sparrow fart this morning and hardly slept a snozz last night, knowing, with the utmost glee, that I was getting out today. I'd waved goodbye and blown a kiss to Mucky Mindy on my cell wall, torn from page eleven of *Snazzle* twat mag. I gave Mindy a little thought and then smiled as I looked around and out of the window. We were about two miles from Leeds. Yes, man, nearly home sweet home.

It was a Friday, but I'd told Katie that I wasn't getting

released until Monday, give her a nice surprise. She'd be chuffed to smithereens to see me saunter through the door.

The train pulled into Leeds station and it took me what seemed like six eternities to get from my platform to the outside concourse. I grabbed half a dozen red roses from a woman with a flower barrow, and I dived into a black and white taxi, more expensive than private hire but fuck them, man, it'd be a dog's age before one of those cunts came.

I had a see-through prison-issue plastic bag with my belongings in. They're cunts like that, the nick, they give you a bastard transparent bag, with giant blue letters saying HMP, just to show you up, the fuckers. I squeezed it really small and hid the logo so that the taxi driver couldn't see it. I didn't want him to know I'd just got out of the shovel, man, he might not have taken me home.

Anyway, he took me, no problem, drove as slow as a motherfucker, didn't matter though, I knew I'd be home soon, to my Katie. He didn't say a word for the three miles to my house. It seemed as though he couldn't speak a stroke of English except "where to" and "six quids" in some sort of Iranian or summat. I wasn't bothered. I took the time to gaze upon the mean streets that I'd missed so much. Everywhere looked new, ha, can you believe that? I hadn't been gone that long and everything seemed to have changed. On the drive home I thought about poor Shuffles and nobody turning up to his funeral, I thought about poor Steve not getting out for Jesus knows how long, and I thought about getting back to DJing and partying and, of course, I thought about my Katie. Will she have missed me? Course she would. Would she throw me around the living room like a love-starved sex kitten? Course she would. Then, like a hammer to the back of my skull, I had the maddest thought, the kind that only blokes just getting out of jail get. The kind of thought where she hasn't missed me at all, no sir, the exact opposite of missed me. The kind of thought where Katie had said, 'Fuck him, he's inside. I'm not gonna suffer.' The kind of thought where she's been getting pounded out like yesterday's beef by every man and his big black brother.

No, man, I don't like these thoughts. Stop it, Gaz, she's not like that, she's sweet, she's loyal, she's faithful.

I hope.

The taxi pulled up outside my gaff and I looked up to the windows. All the curtains were closed, bedrooms and everywhere.

Aw man, this doesn't look good. It's one thirty in the afternoon, she can't be still in bed. Can she?

I paid the taxi gadge, who by the way didn't say please or thank you or kiss my arse, grabbed my shitty, see-through bag and walked slowly to my front door. It was open, so I snuck in really quiet, to surprise her, praying to Good Jesus and all His Angels and Saints that she wasn't in there getting annihilated by Big Winston or someone. That would *not* be nice.

At all.

I gingerly walked down my hallway to the living room. I could hear the telly, nothing else, just the telly, *not* Big Jamaal or Heaven knows what sort of scenario I had in my head. I burst the door open and shouted, 'Surprise!' and there she was, lying on the sofa, in her white bathrobe, watching telly, some sort of woman's romantic comedy. Not getting porno stabbed by the rugby team!

She looked surprised, half a smile at first, shock probably, then she jumped up and hugged me.

'I didn't think you were back till Monday, you little get.'

'Thought I'd surprise you, didn't I? Here you are, love.' I passed her the roses, then pulled her back to me and, 'I've missed you, love, you don't realise,' and squeezed her tight.

She dropped her robe, pulled me onto the sofa and, well, you can guess what happened next. I'd just spent nearly seven months splodging into a spunk-filled, fungus-ridden shower tray, so, yeah, you can guess.

Was it like the Thunders of Odin and the Raging Seas of Hardcore Porn? Er, no. Barely a minute had gone and it was all over! Oh well, it had been a long time.

Katie didn't seem that bothered though, *very* not bothered. It was almost as though she'd done it out of duty rather than love and excitement. She just wiped herself on the bottom of her bathrobe and then, instead of 'I've missed you. Do you want a drink?' or any such sort of thing, she came out with, 'Listen, Gaz love.' She looked serious now. Aw man, she was gonna tell me that she'd been ruptured incessantly by a muscle-bound tennis coach or summat. No. Not that.

She didn't.

'Gaz love, don't say anything yet, let me speak. I've done some thinking while you've been gone, real thinking. And it's like this. I don't wanna be with you anymore.'

I was wiping my cock on the bottom of her robe and started to pipe up to say something but she carried on, 'Gaz, let me finish, please love, I don't wanna be with you, not as long as you're like this. It's not you. It's just not. You're not a jailbird, you're a nice guy. You're not a drug-dealing bad boy, not really. Everyone says that you're a womaniser, but I know you're not, not since you've been with me anyway. So, Gaz, here's the deal, love, I don't wanna be with you, *unless*, unless you change. I want you to stop going partying all the time, I will too. I want you stop taking drugs, I will an' all. I want you stop selling drugs, and I want you to get a proper job. And that's that. If you can do those few simple things, then, and only then, Gaz love, have we got any sort of future. Gemma loves you like a dad, but I don't need her growing up around all that shit, Gaz, I really don't. I want you to stay, I love you, but they're the rules, so there you go.' I looked at her, tried to pull her close but she pulled away, 'I'm serious, Gaz, I can't take it like it was before.'

I perched myself in the armchair and paused for a few moments, taking it all in, then:

'So, baby, does that mean you don't want me to DJ anymore?' I was mortified at the prospect of not DJing. I'd always planned to hang up the mic when I was forty. Nobody wants to see a silly, grey-haired old cunt prancing about like Mick Jagger when they go on a night out. Unless you're off to see the Rolling Stones.

But shit, man, I'm only thirty-two, I can't hang up the mic just yet.

'No, don't give it up, Gaz man, not altogether anyway. Just get a proper job and DJ at the odd wedding or birthday here and there. If you get a residency you'll be back at it every weekend, Gaz, drugs and all that bollocks. You know you will. Do it, do it for me.'

She was right. If I returned to DJing full time, I'd be partying like it was 1999, which it was, but you know what I mean. I'd be back on the drug and club scene in no time, Steve or no Steve.

Yeah, fuck it, I can do that, what's to lose? I can be settled down, man, just me, Katie, my three kids, Dom, Jake and Daisy, and not forgetting little Gemma. Yeah, I can picture it, it'll be like the *Little House on the Prairie*.

So I did, I made my love promise to Katie, to change, to live a "normal" life, and I was gonna set about it the very next day.

But first, where's that bag of Charlie I hid before I went away?

6TH MARCH 1999 — THE VERY NEXT DAY

Whether I agreed with it or not, this was a good time to go "normal". Between 1999 and 2005 Leeds was like Baghdad, man, it was the Wicky, Wicky, Wild, Wild West on steroids, people getting shot up all over the place, man. Prominent crime figures were being killed centre, right, left and up and down. It was crazy. I was glad, very glad, to be out of it. There were almost five thousand murders in the UK during that period, half of those drug related, and half of those in West Yorkshire. Fuck that crazy London Town, they were pussy cats compared to the mad bastards up here. Although I had only ever been small fry in the criminal underworld, in no way a big player, it was still scary to think you could easily get caught up in the criss-cross blast of stray bullets with no particular names on them. All you had to do to maybe get accidentally shot was be in the place that these arch felons frequented, and in the past I had. I'd sat with them, laughed with them, snorted slice with them, slurped the finest cognac with them. And now, they were dead. Murdered. Shot. Stabbed. For God only knows what. Money. Skanked. Disrespected. Fuck knows, no-one really needed an excuse to blow someone's shit away in that crazy time. But you wanna know the real reason everyone was going all Al Capone on each other? I'll tell you.

Coke.

Cocaine. Sniff. Snort. Snozz. Bugle. Slice.

Whatever the fuck you wanted to call it, it fucked everyone up. No-one was happy anymore, not like with Es and whizz, no hugging now, man. No wanting to cuddle your neighbours, nah man. Everyone just wanted to be Tommy Ten Men. Everyone wanted to be Tony Montana mang. Fuck Gaspar Gomez and fuck the fucking Diaz Brothers! It was a common mantra. Everyone in the underbelly of Leeds wanted to be Scarface. Well, not me, man, I was only small time, and I was getting out. Going straight. Being "normal". It was the only way forward. Wasn't it?

So here I am, suited and booted, headed into town to get a "proper" job. And I did. Within twenty minutes of reaching the city centre, I was the proud owner of a new position in Suit Land.

Yep, I got a job as a suit salesman. Katie was chuffed, she loved me again, and I got to sell suits, measuring fuckers up, inside legs and bollock-cupping. Listening to my co-worker, Mad John, who was allergic to bees and wanted to retire to Barbados and eat "untold fruit".

It went on, and on, selling, measuring, cupping, listening, Barbados, fruit, bees, cupping…

All day.

Every fucking day.

And that was that, man. Three weeks later I jacked, left. It wasn't me, man.

It just wasn't me.

APRIL 1999

Katie was cranky that I'd bailed on the Suit gaff, but I assured her I'd sort summat out.

And I did.

Next job, barman at the Rail Station Arms. It was okay I suppose, for three weeks. Then I jacked.

It just wasn't me.

MAY 1999

Katie was cranky again. What the fuck's wrong with her man? I'll get another job. And I did.

Next stop, Bryce, Quarterhouse and Ropers, a world leading accountancy firm. I blagged a job with them, boring as fuck like, typing, filing, staring at charts, staring out of windows, looking at porn on the new invention that was the Internet, talking to cunts who've never been kissed, listening to even more cunts who've never been kissed, looking at more porn and general dogs-bodying, but in the words of my dad, Hulk Dad, "a proper job", the kind of job he always dreamed for me.

For three weeks.

Then I jacked.

It just wasn't me.

JUNE 1999

I tried everything, man, butcher and baker and fucking candlestick maker, nowt was for me though.

I did the occasional DJ spot – weddings, funerals, birthdays, kids' parties, kids' *fucking* parties! But I missed having a regular spot, a place people would associate with me, with DJ Gaz. Now I was no-one. Gaz Nobody. Wherever I lay my P45 that's my home.

It just wasn't me.

Something had to give. I'm a firm believer that "All Good Things Come To Those Who Wait".

And it did.

I landed a job as a bank manager!

Ha! I'm not shitting you, man, I blagged the application form, said I hadn't been in trouble and what not, and next minute, there's me. A bank manager. Fuck me, three months ago I was locked up with bank *robbers*! Funny how shit works out.

To be fair, it wasn't initially as a manager, and it wasn't quite a bank. It was as a telesales cunt with a car insurance firm that was owned by one of the biggest banks in the world. But in the eyes of Katie, and of Hulk Dad, I'd finally "made it". I had the proper job that *they'd* hoped for me, and I was bringing in proper, regular, normal wages.

I lasted a lot more than three weeks in this bastard though. I was determined, even though it wasn't really me, to make it work.

And make it work I did.

Within three months I was the top salesman in my department. Like the legendary boxer Muhammad Ali said, "Whatever job you do, be the *best*, whatever the job. If you're a boxer, be the best boxer. If you're a toilet cleaner, be the *best* toilet cleaner." So I did. I became the best.

ONE YEAR LATER – JULY 2000

Still the best. Bar none.

Earning shitloads of bonus each month, going on sunny holidays three times a year.

Bored out of my fucking brain.

ANOTHER BASTARD YEAR LATER – SEPTEMBER 2001

Still the best salesman, so good in fact that I was promoted to manager. I was now officially a "bank manager", of sorts Anyhoo.

More money, more foreign holidays.

More boredom.

Even watching the Twin Towers coming down on the television in the office canteen was going over my head. A world-changing event, occurring right in front of my eyes and all I could think was, *I'm bored.*

I continued to write to Steve in the nick, telling him how I'd changed, got a good job, stopped taking drugs, stopped partying and blah blah cunting blah.

He wrote back, same as always:

"Gaz man, you're full of shit."

SUMMER 2002

I've always said that "only boring people get bored" and I still maintain that to this day, but you know what? I was bored, I was bored and I was boring.

Steve got out the nick, but he was trying to follow the same route as me and keep on the straight and narrow, so I very rarely saw him. We had the occasional blowout together, but those occasions were very few and far between, man.

I bumped into some girl in Leeds City Centre after work one day. I didn't recognise her from Adam's apple, but she knew me, sort of. Her words to me, in my suit and with my business briefcase, were:

'Hey, didn't you *used* to be DJ Gaz? You used to be cool, man.' And off she fucking trotted, as though she hadn't just shattered my world, with not a care in hers.

I wasn't cool anymore.

This definitely was not me.

But it would be, for four more years.

Four long, dreary, grey, albeit fairly affluent, but still long and bastard monotonous years.

AUGUST 2003

Katie asked me to marry her! Yep, SHE asked ME! I said yeah, we got married, and the plan, as with all marriages I expect, was to live Happily Ever After.

We didn't.

I was bored.

She could tell.

She was bored.

I could tell.

Boredom, as shit as it is, can be very contagious. But still we carried on.

SUMMER 2004

Still a manager, still at the same firm, still married, still in a life-draining quagmire of soul destruction.

I was just sat about, as John Lennon said, "Watching the Wheels."

WINTER 2005

This is fucking killing me now, Katie too, we can both see it, we just don't say it. The kids are blissfully unaware of anything, they're kids. They get taken nice places, they get nice shit, they love life, they're kids. But so am I, a thirty-eight-year-old kid, trapped in an adult world. An adult world with responsibilities and shit that I don't like.

It is *NOT FUCKING ME!*

SUMMER 2006

We'd been living in the flat now for over twelve years, a nice flat, of course, but the neighbours were horrible, smack heads and skanks and pimps and God knows what else. We had a few quid now, we both had good jobs, horrible jobs but fairly well paid, so we moved. We moved to a great big fuck off detached house, a dream after living in the flat, detached with no neighbours, no cunts to destroy our "idyllic" *Little House on the Prairie* life.

As lovely as it was, it didn't alter how we felt towards each other. Sure, we loved each other, but it was getting more like sister and brother every day, she wasn't really interested in "eroticism" anymore. Didn't bother me, she was my wife and that's the way it is sometimes. Isn't it? You love each other and get on with shit. Bored or not.

But I was like a caged lion, man, a caged lion that was fuckin' sick to death of bastard IKEA!

Then, one day, out of the blue, or as Bob Dylan would say, a *Simple Twist of Fate*, an old friend of mine, Barry Westlake, rang me. He'd just bought a pub around the corner from our house, The Naughty Nun. Anyhoo, the day he called I was feeling particularly bored and down. Even though I had the good job, the gorgeous wife, the model kids, and the big detached house, I was feeling pretty worthless. Something I had *never* felt in my life. *Ever.*

It was nice to hear Barry's voice.

'Hi, is that Gaz?' He sounded cheery.

'Yeah man, is that you, Barry? Long time no hear, my old pal, what you up to?' I got a little cheery too, hearing him. He was a funny gadge.

'I won't beat about the bush, Gaz pal, I've just bought The Naughty Nun, do you know it?'

'Yeah course I do, Barry man, it's just round the corner from my house. How's it going, bud?'

'It's going really good, Gaz man, can't complain at all, pal. Only thing is I need a DJ, a good DJ, every weekend. I heard you'd retired but thought I'd give you a try anyway. Know what I mean? Anyway, Gaz man, I can't pay a lot of dough, we can discuss that, but it'll be a laugh, you'll get free beer, and, *and*, it's full of fanny! So, what do you think, Gaz? Do you fancy it?'

I paused for a few moments. I was sitting on my sofa. I looked across the room and Katie was staring into the telly, half watching some shite or other, painting her toenails with one hand, glugging wine with the other, oblivious to my very existence. Gemma was out with her pals. Dom, Jake and Daisy were with their mother, and I was here, with this proposition from Barry.

I was only silent for a few seconds as I looked around my living room, at Katie, at the shite on the fifty inch telly, at her toenails, at my expensive, overstuffed leather furniture. My mind's eye wandered, a rush came over my whole body. It felt like 1985 all over again, like Monday nights at Tiffany's, like the long, hot summers of childhood, like the church disco, like me and Mel, like me and Steve, like the crazy fucking '90s, like the thousands of faceless women, like the boy that never grew up, like, like, The Legendary DJ Gaz.

'Do I fancy it? *Fuckin' right I do. When do I start?*'

—

ΞPILOGUΞ

Have I got any regrets? The dictionary definition for "regret" is "distress or sorrow following a disappointment, repentance or remorse felt for one's wrongdoing or mistakes".

So. Have I got any regrets? What's the point?

You can't change the past, can you?

You can only learn from it.

If you want to.

Everything that ever happened to me or those around me was orchestrated by me in one way or another. Fuck fate. Fuck destiny. The way that things map out is your own doing, not anyone else's.

For all the violence, the hurt, the broken hearts, the lives torn apart, the drugs, the drink, the women, the music, the pure and utter hedonism, would I do it all differently given a second chance?

Would I *fuck*!

There are all these social workers and psychoanalysts and do-gooders in the world. The ones who tell you that kids who turn to crime, take drugs and sleep around must be from deprived backgrounds or broken homes or the blah blah bastard blah.

Well get this, people…

I did it coz I fuckin' *loved* it. Simple as.

SUMMER 1972

I was five years old, lying on my belly with my elbows on the carpet, resting my chin in my hands. I was pretending to watch *Love Thy Neighbour* on the telly, in reality I was listening to my mam and dad chatting to each other, laughing and joking and talking about films.

'That was a great film, Jackie. *The French Connection* it was called. Bloody great film.' My dad had been to the cinema with his mate and was telling my mam about it.

'Yeh, what was it about?' She didn't like the same films as my dad, but she acted interested anyway.

He sounded excited as he told her the plot. 'Well, this cop, Popeye Doyle, has to infiltrate a drugs dealer in France…' I was listening intently, whilst still staring at the telly, 'and the cop is just as much of a villain as the bad guys, if not worse. Mad car chase and everything. It's great.'

My mam still acts interested. 'So, does he catch him in the end? The cop that's worse than the drugs dealer?'

My dad shakes his head. 'Nope! He gets away from him. They'll *have* to make a sequel, sure they will.'

He got up from the sofa and bent down to pick me up, and he placed his giant Hulk hands around my waist and lifted me above his head, laughing and tickling my sides.

'How are ya, little man?' He was smiling at me as I looked down on him from above, my little bum nearly touching the ceiling. 'What do you wanna be when you grow up, eh? Do you wanna be a policeman? Just like Popeye Doyle?'

I looked down at him and gave him the cutest, cheekiest, almost knowing smile.

'No, Daddy… I wanna be a *drugs dealer!*'

He put me down, placed his face in his palms and walked to the kitchen. The radio was playing as he entered shaking his head. The song playing was Cher – *Gypsies, Tramps and Thieves.*

Daz Courtney was born and raised in Leeds. He was educated at various schools in Leeds, culminating at St Michael's College, after which he studied Business at Airedale and Wharfedale. He was all set to start a journalism degree at university. But in 1985, just a few weeks before he was due to start his course, he 'accidentally' became a DJ. This made him forgo his studies and he quickly became a successful DJ and popular face on the scene around Leeds in the 80s and 90s. *Nine Foot Tall* is his first novel, based in part, around his experiences during this time and the places he worked and frequented.

—
ACKNOWLEDGEMENTS

Anyone who has ever written a novel, would have you believe that it is a solitary affair, a lonesome journey, it's not.

Forget the image of the tortured author, sitting alone by candlelight, a near empty bottle of Scotch on his desk, suffering for his art, that vision is for the birds man!

My writing journey was on a road filled with laughter and love, and the people that created that laughter and love helped me to create Nine Foot Tall.

I must start by thanking my publisher, The Book Guild, and all concerned with the production of my book, for believing in Little Daz from Leeds, thank you.

Thanks in abundance goes out to my late mother Jackie, who believed in EVERYTHING I did, or said! Bless her. My dad, Hulk Dad, John, for being my hero, as all dads are to their sons. My siblings, Julie, Nick and Ben, for laughing at everything I ever say or do, and believing nearly everything I tell them. My children, Tom, for working tirelessly to help me get this project off the ground, and laughing at my every word, Josh, for believing in me, believing my tall stories, and also laughing at everything I ever say, Rosie, for her fabulous marketing photos and laughing at everything I ever say, and Jaime, for laughing at everything I ever say!

I must give thanks to all the singers, bands, groups, acts, dj's, pubs, clubs and bars of the 80's and 90's who gave me so much enjoyment and influenced a mammoth part of my life.

A big thank you should go to my dear departed pal, Shaun Melody, taken far too soon, a man who helped to shape my life, and my outlook on it. Thank you Blue Eyes, you lived your life like a shooting star, fast and short-lived, but filled with brightness and wonder, inspiring awe in all who set eyes on you.

And of course, a thank you of gargantuan proportions must go out to my wife, Suzie, who came into my world at just the right time and possibly saved my life. She taught me how to love again, and encouraged me to continue with my writing, both of which I had almost given up on. For this, My Suzie, My Suzie, My very own Suzie, I love you and I thank you.